VALMIKI'S
RAMAYANA

Edited by
M.D. Gupta
Prashant Gupta

Artwork by
Kishan Lal Verma

Conceived by
Ved Prakash

Published By

DREAMLAND PUBLICATIONS

J-128, KIRTI NAGAR, NEW DELHI - 110 015, (INDIA)
Fax : 011-543 8283 **Tel :** 011 - 543 5657
E-mail : dreamland@vsnl.com

First published in 1998 by
Dreamland Publications
J-128, Kirti Nagar, New Delhi- 110 015 (India)
Fax : 011-543 8283, Tel.: 011-543 5657

ISBN 81-7301-254-7
Reprint 1999

Processing by
Rave Scans

Printed at :
Dewan Offset Printers (P) Ltd.
D. N. Offset Printers

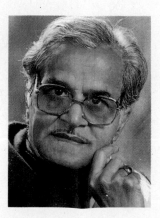

Sh. Kishan Lal Verma,
Born in Delhi, is one of India's well known
Illustrators. He specializes in the pictures of Human
Anatomy and Human relation. There is no field left in
Commercial Art which is not covered by his excellence.
He has worked for so many advertising agencies, magazines
and other publishing firms. He has also done some
outstanding works for Children's Books and religious books
such as Mahabharta etc.

Now we are publishing his marvellous creative
work on Ramayana. We hope that this book will leave a
lasting impression on everybody.

—Publisher

INTRODUCTION

The RAMAYANA and the MAHABHARATA are two most important epics of ancient India. The Ramayana is the older of the two and was authored by Maharishi Valmiki at the instance of Sage Narada.

The word—**Ramayana**—means *life-story of Rama*. The original work was in Sanskrit, though later on, Saint Tulsi Das wrote it in Hindi poetry under the title RAMCHARITMANAS.

For our readers' convenience, this epic has been divided into eight episodes. These episodes are as under :

1. The Childhood Episode
2. The Ayodhya episode
3. The Forest Episode
4. The Kishkindha episode
5. The Fascinating Episode
6. The Lanka Episode
7. The Uttara Episode
8. Lava-Kusha Episode

In South India, *Kamban* wrote the Ramayana in Tamil while *Kirtivasa* wrote it in Bengali.

As remarked by Saint Narada, the Ramayana came to be a sacred book. People study it with deep devotion and reverence not only in India but in some countries of the Far East too.

Because of its highly lesson-giving ideals, the Ramayana has been serving as a light-house for the people of India. Its ideals of true family-relationships, dutifulness, purity in thinking, tolerance and virtue are working a wonder even today in the face of polluting western influences which are more concerned with materialism than with noble values.

CONTENTS

(THE CHILDHOOD EPISODE)
1. DASHRATHA WORSHIPPING THE SUNGOD

The solar Dynasty (Surya Vansha) began with Vaivaswata Manu who was the son of the Sun-God. Manu was also the first ruler of mankind.

It was Ikshvaku, Manu's eldest son, who built the city of Ayodhya on the banks of the holy river Sarayu. Since then Ayodhya remained the capital of all the great and glorious kings born in the solar Dynasty like the truthful Harishchandra, Sagar, Bhagiratha, Daleep, Raghu, Aja and Dashratha, the great and Lord Rama Himself.

With the passage of time the solar Dynasty became famous with the name of Raghu Dynasty (RaghuVansha) by virtue of the *Sarva Dakshina Yajna* performed by the great Emperor Raghu who gave his all in charity except the clothes on his body.

The great Dashratha was the grandson of the famous Raghu. He inherited all the virtues of his great and glorious ancestors and (had) many more of his own. He was so strong that he had no enemies. He was as wealthy as Indra and Kubera put together. He was a Royal Sage almost as good as a Maharsi.

2. SON-GRANTING YAJNA

Dashratha had only one regret that he had got no son so far. So the famous Rishyasringa was invited to perform the Yajna to beget a son. As the Yajna was going on in Ayodhya, Devas were holding a conference in heaven. They begged Lord Vishnu to be born as four sons of King Dashratha who was then performing a sacrifice for progeny. As the Ghee was poured into the sacred fire, flames shot up. From out of the flames came a sunny bright figure holding a bowl of gold in its hands. Calling king Dashratha by his name, the figure said, "The Devas are pleased with you. Here is Paayasam (Kheer) sent by the gods for your wives. If they eat it, they will bear four glorious sons for you."

With joy unbounded, Dashratha received the bowl as he would receive a child.

3. THE QUEENS TAKING KHEER PRASAD

Having sought the permission of his enlightened Guru sage Vasishtha, Dashratha hurried to his palace. He gave half of the Kheer Prasad to his eldest queen Kaushalya. The remaining half was divided into two equal parts. One part was given to Sumitra and the other was given to Kaikeyee. Since Kaikeyee was the last to receive the Kheer Prasad, she lost her temper and spoke some harsh words to Dashratha.

That very moment by Lord Shankara's grace an eagle pounced upon Kaikeyee's palm and flew away with the Kheer Prasad to the Anjan mountain where Anjani was meditating on Lord Shankara to beget a son like the lord himself. The eagle placed that Prasad on the open palms of Anjani whose eyes were closed in meditation. She ate it thinking it to be a gift from Lord Shiva.

Kaushalya and Sumitra shared their kheer with Kaikeyee. All the three queens became pregnant.

4. THE QUEENS CONCEIVE

As soon as Dashratha came to know that the queens had conceived by Virtue of the kheer Prasad, he was beside himself with joy. He felt as if he had got everything in the world. His face brightened up. He thanked all the gods in the heaven. Above all he worshipped the sun-god with great devotion and dedication. Now he felt sure that the Solar Dynasty would go on by the blessings of the sun god.

King Dashratha prostrated at the holy feet of his revered Guru Sage Vasishtha and told him the happy news. The sage advised the king that during the period of Pregnancy he should fulfil all the desires of the queens. Dashratha was glad enough to carry out the advice of his learned Guru.

5. BIRTH OF FOUR SONS

All the queens were glad at heart since they became pregnant. They were all very happy. From the time Lord Vishnu found His way into the womb, joy and prosperity reigned in all the three worlds. In the palace shone the queens who were all mines of beauty, virtue and glory. Time rolled on happily till the moment arrived for the Lord to be revealed.

The whole creation, animate and inanimate, was full of delight as Lord Rama, the very source of joy and bliss, was going to come down to the earth. It was the ninth day of the bright half of the sacred month of Chaitra. The sun was in the middle of the sky as it was noon time. But it was neither cold nor hot. A cool, soft and fragrant breeze was blowing. The gods were feeling exhilarated and the saints were bubbling with enthusiasm.

Kaushalaya gave birth to Rama, Kaikeyee to Bharata and Sumitra to two sons Lakshmana and Shatrughana.

6. THE FOUR SONS PLAYING

Thirteen days after the advent of the Lord, the naming ceremony was performed by the enlightened sage Vasishtha. The eldest son was named 'Rama' as He is the very embodiment of joy and bliss for the whole universe. The second son was named Bharata as he sustains and supports the universe. The third son was named 'Shatrughana', the destroyer of enemies. The fourth son was given the splendid name of Lakshmana as he is the abode of noble virtues, the beloved of Lord Rama and the base of the whole universe. The four parents enjoyed the sweet lisping prattle and pranks of their four elegant, resplended and divine sons. They were full of bliss. The whole of Ayodhya was full of joy unspeakable.

7. DASHRATHA SUPERVISING ARCHERY TRAINING

King Dashratha was the greatest archer of his times. He was a Atiratha who could fight a number of Maharathas alone. He was such a perfect bowman as could shoot an invisible man simply by hearing his voice. Sharavan Kumar who came to the river to fetch water was shot dead in ignorance by Dashratha because of the gurgling sound of the pitcher which gave the impression of an elephant drinking water.

So Dashratha thought of imparting the knowledge and skill of archery to his four sons under his own supervision. He wished them to become as perfect bowmen as he himself was. So with great love, affection and accuracy, he watched his sons' skills and tactics of shooting arrows to hit the desired targets. His brave and eager sons learnt the art of archery in the shortest possible time.

11

8. VASISHTHA WITH THE FOUR PRINCES

When all the four brothers attained to boyhood, the preceptor as well as their parents invested them with the sacred thread. Then they were sent to the hermitage of sage Vasishtha for their formal education.

In ancient India it was the tradition that a student whether he happened to be a prince or a pauper would have to join the simple hermitage of his learned Guru to get education and learning. Unless one sits at the holy feet of his enlightened teacher, one can't learn anything worthwhile.

Although Rama Himself is God, yet He too needs a Guru when He comes down to this earth. This is an illusion. He who is born in this world is influenced by its illusory nature to some extent.

As all the four brothers were endowed with wisdom and virtues, they mastered the Vedas and learnt all other disciplines needed for princes in a short span of time.

9. VASISHTHA IN MEDITATION

Sage Vasishtha who was a man of great realization and renunciation would sit in meditation daily without fail for a pretty long time in the early hours before the day dawned. That is why he was such a great Guru. He was established in Brahman or Godhood.

His heart was as pure as the waters of the Ganga in those ancient times. Although Vishwamitra had burnt his hundred sons to ashes yet he did not harbour any malice in his heart towards him. Once Vasishtha was having spiritual talks with his wife Arundhati who remarked, "How pure is the moon light!" Then Vasishtha retorted, "No doubt about it, but it is not as pure and bright as the Divine Aura or Brahmanhood of Vishwamitra." What a tribute to a person who had caused him so much harm! Vishwamitra who happened to be in his hermitage at that moment heard this praise of his with his own ears. He fell at Vasishtha's feet who embraced him. Since then they became fast friends.

13

10. VASISHTHA TEACHING AT HIS HERMITAGE

The teachings of the divine and enlightened preceptor sage Vasishtha are enshrined in his famous work 'Yoga Vasishtha' which is a mine of spiritual knowledge.

The glory of Ayodhya and that of King Dashratha spread in the three worlds by virtue of the knowledge and education given to his students by the learned sage Vasishtha. It was due to him that the people of Ayodhya were happy, virtuous, learned in sacred lore, free from greed, truthful and contended with their own fortune. No one was sensuous, miserly, cruel and ignorant.

Thanks to Vasishtha the eight Ministers of Emperor Dashratha were so upright and honest in their dealings that they meted out punishment even to their own sons strictly according to the law of the land when occasion demanded it.

Vasishtha asked the four princes to remember that the king in whose kingdom the people are unhappy must go to hell after his death. Had the present day rulers heeded this advice of the great sage, this world would have become a heaven on earth.

11. SUMANTRA MEETS VASISHTHA

When the education of the four princes came to an end, sage Vasishtha informed king Dashratha that they should be carried back to the palace. Sumantra was sent to fetch the four sons. He took with him royal robes for the princes.

Having reached the hermitage, Sumantra touched the holy feet of the great Guru and stood before him with folded hands.

The sage blessed him and inquired of him about the welfare of the king, the queens and the people of Ayodhya.

Then he sent for the four princes.

12. PRINCES PROSTRATE AT GURU'S FEET BEFORE LEAVING FOR AYODHYA

Rama, Lakshmana, Bharata and Shatrughan prostrated at the holy feet of their learned and revered Guru who had been instrumental in bringing about their physical, mental, intellectual and spiritual development. The Guru lifted them and hugged them to his bosom. He gave them all what had remained with him by his blessed embrace and a glance of his divine eyes.

Then he asked them to get ready to leave for Ayodhya. The princes felt somewhat sad to depart from their beloved and learned Guru. But soon they conquered this feeling of sadness as their Guru had taught them this great art of living. They had become the masters of their minds.

13. THE PRINCES RETURN

Now the four princes clad themselves in the royal robes which had been brought for them from the palace by Sumant, the wise. They also put on their crowns and other precious ornaments which were meant for them. They bowed low towards the hermitage of the sage and mounted the chariot. They were now eager to see their mothers, father and the people of Ayodhya.

The swift horses soon reached the city of Ayodhya where people thronged on either side of the road to give a warm reception to their noble and glorious princes. The whole city had been decorated like a bride. People were delighted and elated to have a glimpse of Rama, Lakshmana, Bharata and Shatrughana. There were great rejoicings here, there and everywhere.

14. COMING HOME FROM THE HERMITAGE

As soon as the chariot reached the gates of the palace, Rama was the first to alight from it. The three younger brothers followed suit.

Rama first of all, touched the feet of mother Kaikeyee who hugged him to her bosom out of great affection. Then he fell at the feet of Sumitra and his mother Kaushalya. Bharata, Lakshmana and Satrughana touched the feet of the three mothers. Then the four princes led by Rama fell at the feet of their father Dashratha whose joy knew no bounds. The whole palace beamed with happiness. Generous alms were given to the poor. Rama, the crown-prince, guided his brothers in the matters of state. He taught them how to be righteous and virtuous. Rama is the very embodiment of Dharma. He observes norms for the welfare of society. The purpose of his coming down to earth as a human being was to kill Ravana that resides in every heart in the form of lust, greed, anger and arrogance.

15. VISHWAMITRA DEMANDS RAMA AND LAKSHMANA

King Dashratha was happy to see his four sons grow up valiant, virtuous, brave and amiable.

One day the king was thinking of his sons' marriage when a messenger announced the arrival of the great sage Vishwamitra who was feared by all the sages of those days.

Dashratha stepped down from his throne. He fell at Vishwamitra's feet and said, "I am truly blessed. Your arrival is due to the merit of my ancestors. Is there anything I can do for you ? Command and I shall obey."

Vishwamitra was rejoiced to hear these words of king Dashratha and his face brightened. He said, "O King, your words are worthy of you."

16. RAMA AND LAKSHMANA WITH VISHWAMITRA

Vishwamitra said, "I am performong a Yajna or sacrifice. Two powerful demons Mareecha and subahu defile it by showering blood and bones on the sacred fire. My troubles will end if you send with me the eldest of your sons Rama who can kill all the powerful demons."

Dashratha shuddered at the demand out of fear and anxiety. He stood speechless as he was bewildered and stunned. Sage Vasishtha said, "O king ! Have no fear. Send Rama with the sage along with Lakshmana. Vishwamitra is the bravest of the brave and wisest of the wise. None can equal him in the three worlds in martial or spiritual prowess. He has come for the good of your sons."

17. TAADAKA KILLED

Having crossed the Ganga, Vishwamitra along with Rama and Lakshman made their difficult way through a dense forest made dreadful by the resounding roar of wild beasts. It was the Dandaka forest. For long people lived there happily till Taadaka and her son Mareecha wrought havoc and changed it into a dreadful wilderness.

Vishwamitra warned Rama and Lakshamana, "Taadaka and Mareecha are still here in this forest. None dare enter it for fear of Taadaka. She has the strength of a thousand elephants. Her atrocities are intolerable. You must kill her to make this area safe for the sages."

Rama twanged his bow. The whole forest resounded with its sound. Racing with anger Taadaka ran in the direction whence the sound came and sprang upon Rama. The battle began. Rama pierced her chest with a deadly arrow. The huge and ugly monster fell down lifeless. The Devas cheered. Vishwamitra embraced Rama and blessed him.

18. AHALYA REDEEMED

The Yajna having been protected from Subahu and Mareecha, Sage Vishwamitra carried the two brothers to the capital city of Mithila where Janaka, the illustrious philosopher king, was going to hold the *Swayambar* of his dear daughter Sita.

On the way they saw a beautiful deserted hermitage where sage Gautama used to live with his wife Ahalya in peace and holy meditation. One day Indra disguised as Gautama entered the hut of the sage in his absence to have sexual union with the beautiful Ahalya who was vain of her beauty. Having committed the sin, god Indra fled out of the cottage in guilty panic but was bumped into sage Gautama who cursed him to become a eunuch.

Then Gautama cursed his erring wife, "Living on air, you shall stay here, unseen by any one till Lord Rama visits this place."

As Rama set foot in the *Aashrama*, the curse was lifted and Ahalya stood before him in all her beauty. True penitence has such a power.

19. KING JANAK WELCOMES VISHWAMITRA

Now the great sage Vishwamitra along with Rama and Lakshmana advanced towards Mithila, the capital of Videha Janaka. King Janaka was known as 'Videha' as he would be unaware of his body and its demands when he dived into the ocean of inner bliss surging within his bosom. Verily he was a sage-king. As soon as Janaka saw Lord Rama, he was beside himself with joy super-natural. Bowing his head at the sage's feet, he inquired who those two princes were. The sage smilingly answered, "They are the sons of king Dashratha. They have come with me to see the 'Swayambar' of your daughter Sita."

20. JANAKA UTTERING HARSH WORDS

Then king Janaka carried them to the site of the 'Swayambar' where the bow-sacrifice was to take place. Countless kings and princes had assembled there from all parts of India to win the hand of Sita.

Lord Shiva's bow was so massive and unyielding that even the great champions Ravana and Banasura could not lift it. One by one came forward the valiant princes and kings, but none could even raise it from the ground not to speak of bending, stringing and fitting an arrow to the great bow of Lord Shiva ! Humiliated and dejected, ten thousand kings all at once tried to raise it but the bow did not budge even an inch.

Having seen such a miserable plight of all the suitors, king Janaka was stunned and pained. He got up and said, "I think there is no hero left on this earth. It is not the will of Providence that my daughter Sita should get married. She is destined to remain a Virgin for her whole life. Had I known that the earth was bereft of the brave, I would never have undertaken such a vow."

25

21. LAKSHMANA LOSING HIS TEMPER AT THE INSULTING REMARKS OF JANAKA

Having heard what king Janaka uttered, there was a pindrop silence in that august assembly. But Lakshmana was red with rage. His eyebrows were knit. His lips quivered and his eyes shot fire. Janaka's words had pierced his heart like arrows. Having bowed his head at Lord Rama's lotus-feet, Lakshmana stood up and spoke out, "In an assembly where anyone of Raghu's race is present no one would dare speak such insulting word as Janaka has done. With the permission of Lord Rama, I can lift the round earth like a ball and break it like an earthen jar ! What, then is this wretched old bow ? I can run with it not less than eight hundred miles." At these angry words of Lakshmana the earth shook. Everybody was terrified. But Sita felt delighted.

22. LORD RAMA BREAKS THE BOW

Lord Rama pacified his younger brother Lakshmana and asked him to sit beside him. At such an auspicious moment, sage Vishwamitra spoke in most endearing words, "Up Rama ! Break the bow of Lord Shiva and relieve Janak of his anguish."

On hearing the Guru's words, Rama bowed his head at his feet. There was no joy or sorrow in his heart. But all the saints were delighted. Rama moved towards the bow like a young lion. He lifted it effortlessly as if it were a garland of flowers. Resting one end of the bow against his toe, he bent it and strung it. He drew the string back with such a force that the mighty bow broke into two at the middle. It produced a great noise like the thundering of clouds. The earth shook and a violent earthquake occurred.

23. PARUSRAMA'S ENCOUNTER WITH LAKSHMANA

The deafening sound produced by the breaking of Lord Shiva's bow attracted the attention of sage Parusrama of the Bhrigu dynasty. He came there thundering and roaring with a bow on one shoulder and a battle-axe on the other and with an arrow shining like lightning in his hand. All the kings and princes trembled in fear.

28

24. RAMA PACIFIES PARUSRAMA

Flying into a rage Parusrama spoke in harsh words, "Tell me, O stupid Janaka, who has broken the bow ? Show him at once or else I will destroy the whole of your kingdom." Janaka was too terrified to reply.

At this crucial juncture Lord Rama spoke with folded hands, "My lord ! He who has broken this bow is none but a servant of yours ! Tell me your command." The furious sage Parusrama replied that the breaker of the bow was his sworn enemy and not a servant. He deserved to be killed.

Now was Lakshmana's turn who stood up and said, "I have broken many a small bow in my childhood, but you never grew so angry, my lord. Why are you so fond of this particular bow ?" "O young prince ! Control your tongue. You seem to be in the grip of death."

Then he turned to Rama and said, "Son of Dashratha, here is my bow which is equal in all respects to the one that you broke. Lord Vishnu gave it to my father. If you string this bow, I will bow to you as the Avatar of Lord Vishnu Himself." Rama took the bow and arrow from Parusrama.

In the twinkling of an eye he strung the bow and set the arrow to it. Then he said with a smile, "This mighty Vaishnava arrow must destroy either your powers of locomotion or the fruits of your *Tapas*." Parusrama bowed to Lord Rama and said, "Let this arrow consume all my powers earned through penance or Tapas. But I must hurry back to the Mahendra mountains before the sun sets." Parusrama had realized that his time was over. He exercised his sway upon the earth for a pretty long time. The kings on the earth trembled to hear his name. He had conquered the earth twenty one times having killed the Kshatrias kings. He donated their kingdoms to the Brahmans as he himself was a Brahman. His arrogance kept on increasing and he came to assume himself to be invincible. Lord Rama was born to humble the arrogant who considered themselves to be the mightiest.

25. SITA GARLANDS & WEDS LORD RAMA

After the departure of Parusrama to the mountain forest for penance, the gods sounded their kettledrums and rained down flowers on Lord Rama. Peace and happiness descended in every heart. She held in her lotus hands the fair garland of victory. She stood motionless as a portrait before Lord Rama. Her clever companion exhorted her saying, "Invest the bridegroom with the beautiful wreath of victory. At this Sita garlanded Lord Rama. Witnessing the wreath of victory resting on Lord Rama's bosom, gods showered flowers from heaven. Great sages uttered blessings with shouts of victory.

26. THE MARRIAGE PROCESSION STARTS FROM AYODHYA

After Sita had garlanded her eternal husband Lord Rama, messengers were sent to Ayodhya to inform King Dashratha that his son Rama had won the hand of Sita by breaking Lord Shiva's bow. The king and his noble courtiers were delighted to hear the feat performed by young Rama.

With a large number of followers Dashratha proceeded to Mithila for the wedding ceremony. He took with him abundant riches and precious jewels. The four wings of his army— the horse-riders, chariots, elephants and infantry marched close behind the king as a defensive measure. The sages accompanied the king in their glorious chariots. Driving along the road for four days, the grand marriage procession entered the territory of Mithila.

King Janaka welcomed Dashratha and his men with open arms. Words failed to describe the splendour of the marriage procession. There were magnificent elephants, horses, golden chariots, dancers musicians and men dressed in royal robes. All were in a festive mood.

Gallant princes made their steeds dance with great skill. All the musical instruments were being played upon. Joy and happiness prevailed in the atmosphere.

27. PERFORMANCE OF MARRIAGE

After the reception of the Baraat, preparations were on for the actual wedding ceremony. King Janaka's younger brother Kusadhwaja who was the king of Sankasya had two charming and virtuous daughters Mandavi and Shrutakirti. Vasishtha and Vishwamitra, the jewels among sages, jointly asked for the hand of Mandavi for prince Bharata and that of Shrutakirti for the valiant Shatrughana. Janaka and his younger brother Kusadhwaja felt overjoyed and blessed at this demand. Thus on the same altar Lord Rama was married to Sita, Lakshmana was married to Janaka's younger daughter Urmila, Bharata to Mandavi and Shatrughana was married to Shrutakirti. Precious gifts were given by the two saintly brothers to their four daughters out of sheer love for them.

28. DASHRATHA RETURNING TO AYODHYA

After the wedding had been performed, the eminent sage Vishwamitra forthwith proceeded to the Himalayas. The glorious king Dashratha too turned back to Ayodhya along with his four sons and their newly-wedded brides. Before his departure Dashratha, the generous, bestowed on the Brahmans four lakhs of recently calved cows that had their horns plated with gold and yielded ample milk as well as plenty of other riches. The eternal principle behind this charity is, "If you shower happiness on others, it comes back to you manifold."

As soon as Dashratha with his dear sons and daughters-in-law reached his capital, he was given a warm reception fit for the gods by the citizens of Ayodhya. The whole city had been decorated like a bride. On the advice of Sage Vasishtha, Dashratha worshipped Ganesha, Lord Shiva and goddess Parvati before stepping into the city.

Glorious Queens Kaushalya, Kaikeyee and Sumitra with golden platters of fragrant flowers, sweets and incense worshipped their sons and their charming and virtuous daughters-in-law at the main gate of their magnificent palace. Their hearts were full of heavenly bliss ! Who would not like to witness such a glorious sight !

29. DASHRATHA CONSULTS VASISHTHA

All the princesses or brides hereafter happily enjoyed life with their husbands in their private apartments. Rama and Sita lived happily in Ayodhya for twelve years. Their hearts communed even without speech. One day the heroic Yudhajit, maternal uncle of Bharata and Satrughana came to Ayodhya and took the two princes away with him to his kingdom Kekaya. Considering his old age, Dashratha wished to crown Rama as Prince or Yuvaraja. So he straight away went to the hermitage of his revered Guru and seer Vasishtha to seek his blessings. Vasishtha was glad to hear the king's intention. He advised him to convene a meeting of the Rajya Sabha to seek its approval. The whole assembly of the elite declared with one voice that Rama should be coronated as He is the very embodiment of virtue and valour. He deserved to be crowned for so many reasons. He was an idol of the people who loved him from the core of their hearts.

30. DASHRATHA SENDS FOR RAMA

Having sought the unanimous approval of the Rajya Sabha without even a single dissenting note, King Dashratha asked his Home Minister Sumantra to fetch Rama who was till now ignorant of all these happenings.

Rama came and bowed to his father. The king embraced him and having seated him on the throne beside him spoke out, "Dear son ! I have grown old. I have enjoyed my life as a man and as a king. Now there is nothing left for me to do except to install you on the throne of our fore-fathers to-morrow itself." But that 'To-morrow' came after fourteen years when Dashratha was no more to see his son's coronation. So the Ramayana teaches us, "Do not put off till to-morrow what you can do to-day."

35

31. GURU VASISHTHA ADVISES RAMA

Having instructed Rama in connection with his coronation fixed for to-morrow, Dashratha summoned sage Vasishtha, the family priest. With folded hands he spoke to his Guru thus, "Kindly advise Rama and Sita to observe a fast to-night for their welfare so that all hurdles in coronation are cleared."

The celebrated sage Vasishtha who was well-versed in the Vedas and knew many sacred spells (Mantras) went in person to Rama's palace. Rama came out of the palace bare footed to receive the revered sage at the gate and fell at his holy feet. Rama took the sage into his palace with great reverence and sought his blessings. Vasishtha said, "Dear Rama ! you are going to be a sovereign to-morrow. So you must keep fast for the night with Sita. Keep on chanting these holy Mantras or sacred spells. Sleep on grass spread on the floor."

Rama promised to abide by his advice. Vasishtha then returned to the king.

Rama and Sita practised penance that night. They chanted the sacred Mantras given to them by the learned sage. That night they virtually lived like hermits. Perhaps they had foreseen their fate for the next fourteen years to come. They had already practised their exile in the palace itself.

32. MANTHARA POISONING KAIKEYEE'S EARS

The moment Manthara came to know of Rama's coronation the next day, she rushed to Kaikeyee's palace. She was a hunch-back woman companion and a great confidant of Queen Kaikeyee. Entering her bed chamber Manthara spoke aloud, "Rise, rise, foolish woman ! A flood of misfortune is rising to ruin and drown you ! Your sun is setting ! Dashratha has decided to make Rama the real ruler of this land in the absence of your son Bharata." Kaikeyee was glad to hear Rama's coronation and she gave her necklace to Manthara who threw it to the floor and said, "Insane woman ! From to-morrow your son Bharata will be a subject and a slave. Rama will get him killed. You will be reduced to a status of a maid-servant to Kaushalya."

Now Kaikeyee got terrified and asked Manthara what to do. Manthara said, "Demand the two boons the king promised you. Bharata must be crowned and Rama be exiled for fourteen years. Go now and lie down in the sulking room." Manthara again reminded Kaikeyee to be obstinate and hard-hearted to gain the desired boons.

37

33. KAIKEYEE IN PROTEST CHAMBER

Kaikeyee forthwith entered the sulking room. She clad herself in a dirty saree. She removed all her ornaments and jewels and scattered them on the floor. Then she stretched herself on the floor shedding crocodile tears.

Dashratha went to Kaikeyee's chamber but came to know that she was in the protest chamber. He was surprised and horrified to see her widow like dress and appearance. The old and innocent king tried his best to know the reason of her grief, but Kaikeyee remained as mute as a statue. Then Dashratha said, "I swear in the name of Rama that I will do whatever you desire."

34 KAIKEYEE DEMANDED HER TWO BOONS

The moment king Dashratha swore by Rama, Kaikeyee sat up. She knew her man well. She began boldly, "Do you remember, king, how long ago you fainted on the battlefield in your chariot struck with deadly arrows ? You were about to lose your life. I drove your chariot in the dark night taking you out of the battlefield. Then I removed the arrows from your body. I comforted and revived you. When you regained your consciousness, did you not promise me two boons ?

Dashratha at once replied, "Yes, I do remember everything. Ask for your two boons. You shall have them now."

Kaikeyee heaved a sigh of relief and said, "Be true to your word like your ancestors. My first demand is, 'Crown my son Bharata.' My second demand is, 'Exile your son Rama to live in the Dandaka forest for fourteen years !'

Hearing these two demands of wicked Kaikeyee, Dashratha was thunder-struck. He fell down unconscious.

35. RAMA AND SITA MUSING

When Dashratha recovered from his swoon, he looked at Kaikeyee. Seeing her he trembled like a stag at the sight of a tiger. He sat up on the floor and moaned helplessly. Again he swooned. Having recovered his senses he fell at Kaikeyee's feet and begged of her, "Do not send Rama to the forest. Without water, without sunlight., I may live for a while, but never without Rama !" Truly, no one can live without Rama who is the life breath of every creature. But Kaikeyee was bent upon exiling Rama out of greed and stupidity. In fact, the demons like Ravana and Meghnatha were destined to be destroyed. The whole episode was going to be a blessing in disguise in the long run.

Here Rama and Sita sat in their palace looking forward to the future course of events. Rama, the omniscient, was perhaps getting restless to depart to the forest for the fulfilment of his mission.

36. SUMANTRA SUMMONS RAMA

The king clung to Kaikeyee's feet and prayed, "Is not Rama like Indra himself ? All praise him for his truthfulness, friendliness, learning, wisdom, heroism and humility as well. No one has heard a harsh word from his lips. How can I send him to the forest infested with ferocious wild animals ? Have pity on me in this old age of mine. Ask for anything else on this earth and I will give it to you. I beg you to give me back my Rama. I beg you humbly not to send me to the abode of Death !"The King struggled in a sea of grief but cruel Kaikeyee uttered these harsh words, "If you do not carry out my two demands, I will this very night drink poison and end my life."

Kaikeyee then insisted on sending for Rama at once so that he might be ordered to go to the forest without further delay.

Dashratha groaned, "Well ! Let me see Rama before I breathe my last. Death is staring me in the face. Let Rama come."

Day dawned. The hour fixed for the coronation was approaching. Vasishtha and his disciples with golden vessels full of the waters of holy rivers had reached the palace. Sumantra was sent by sage Vasishtha to arouse the king from his slumber. Kaikeyee ordered Sumantra to fetch Rama at once as the king wished to see him.

Sumantra went to Rama's palace who was getting ready for the coronation. He gave him the message that the king and Queen Kaikeyee wanted his presence. Rama hastened to obey.

37. RAMA FACING KAIKEYEE

As Rama stepped over the threshhold, he saw with awe-struck amazement his father lying on the bare floor in deep grief and anguish. He touched his father's feet and then stood with folded hands before Kaikeyee and said to her, "Mother ! what ails father ?" Kaikeyee replied, "The king, your father, promised me two boons long ago which I demanded last night. My son Bharata should be crowned today and you should go to the forest for fourteen years."

38. INCONSOLABLE DASHRATHA

Kaikeyee was happy and surprised at Rama's willingness and readiness to go to the forest without any hesitation at all. Having touched the feet of his father and Kaikeyee, Rama rushed out of the chamber. Lakshmana who was standing outside followed him.

Rama hurried to mother Kaushalya's palace and falling at her feet spoke thus, "Mother ! Father has crowned me the king of the forest ! Bless me that I protect the kingdom of the forest from the enemies ."What a spirit of cheerful renunciation on the part of Rama ! what a lofty character ! That is why Rama is enshrined in every heart even to-day. May everybody face the sorrows of life as calmly as Rama did. Sita and Lakshmana too got ready to go the forest with Rama. The three went to take leave of the aged king. The king lay flat on the floor, his glory gone and his face distorted with anguish. Rama and Lakshmana made him sit and fell at his feet to seek his blessings and permission.

39. HEART-RENDING SCENE

Rama, Lakshmana and Sita came out of the palace in the guise of hermits and mounted the chariot. Men, women and children of Ayodhya were sobbing and weeping bitterly. They followed the chariot in large numbers as most of them had decided to leave their homes to live in the forest with their beloved Rama.

King Dashratha stepped out of Kaikeyee's palace and looked at the cloud of dust as though he saw in it the beloved form of his Rama. Then he fell down moaning.

40. RAMA LEAVES HIS SUBJECTS STEALTHILY

Not to speak of all kinds of people, even the birds on wings tried to prevent Rama from going to the forest. He was the very embodiment of love.

The chariot stopped on the bank of the river Tamsa. Sumantra unyoked the horses and watered them. Rama offered the evening prayers by the river and said, "Let us fast on this first night of our forest life, Lakshmana. Your presence rids me of all cares."

Lakshmana spread some grass on the ground for Rama and Sita to sleep on. But he himself spent the night in vigil talking with Sumantra.

Long before dawn Rama rose from sleep and said to Sumantra, "The loving citizens of Ayodhya who have followed us are now fast asleep. They shall not let me go ahead if they wake up. Harness the horses and cross the river while they are yet asleep." Sumantra readily obeyed Rama. When the citizens got up in the morning, they could not see Rama and his chariot anywhere. So they returned home abusing Kaikeyee on the way.

45

41. NISHAD WELCOMES RAMA

Sumantra drove the chariot far into the forest. Having crossed many streams the chariot reached the southern boundary of the Kosala country. Here Rama got down the chariot and saluted his motherland Ayodhya with great reverence.

The chariot reached the bank of the holy Ganga. Finding a spot of surpassing charm, Rama said, "We shall spend the night here."

Untying the horses they sat under a tree. Guha, the ruler of this region, was already there with a number of his servants to welcome Rama, Lakshmana and Sita. He had unbounded love for Rama. He was a man of great power and prestige as he was the chieftain of the tribes who lived on the banks of the Ganga. Rama embraced Guha who said with folded hands, "Feel perfectly at home in my kingdom. Kindly spend all the fourteen years with us here. You shall not lack anything, I assure you. Looking after you will be a pleasure and privilege to me. Be kind enough to accept my hospitality."

Rama once again embraced Guha warmly and exclaimed, "Brother, I very well know how much you love me. Your wish is as good as your hospitality. I am bound by my own vows. I must spend fourteen years dwelling in the forest. Pray feed these horses well. Then we shall enjoy simple food and rest for the night."

42. RAMA REQUESTS SUMANTRA TO RETURN TO AYODHYA

Next morning Sumantra bowed low and stood before Rama with folded hands seeking his further commands.

Rama understood Sumantra's unuttered grief. He patted his shoulder with his loving hand and said to him, "Revered Sumantra ! Kindly return now to Ayodhya with all speed and be at the side of the king, my dear father. Now your duty lies in looking after him."

Hearing these words, Sumantra sobbed like a child. Wiping the tears from his eyes, Rama exclaimed, "Our family has known no better friend than you. You alone can console father. Grief has broken his heart. Cheer him by all means. Have no worry about us. Tell the grief-stricken father that we are perfectly hale and hearty and happy in the forest."

Sumantra again wept seeing the empty chariot. Rama consoled him and requested him to do his duty. With a heavy heart the noble Sumantra drove to Ayodhya. As he drove the chariot, the horses turned their eyes towards Rama and neighed.

43. THE BOATMAN WASHES LORD'S FEET

When even animals felt so miserable on being torn away from Rama, how could his subjects and his father and mother hope to live without him ?

Having sent back Sumantra, Rama arrived at the bank of the heavenly stream, the Ganga. He called for a boat, but the ferryman would not bring it. The boatman said, "I know your secret well. The dust of your lotus-feet has the power to change things into human beings. I have heard that a rock was transformed into a charming woman by the touch of your feet. You know wood is not harder than stone. If my boat changes into a woman by the touch of the dust sticking your feet, how shall I support two women without my boat which is the only means of my livelihood ? I will let you board the boat only when I wash your feet with the waters of the Ganga." The all-compassionate Lord Smilingly said, "Very well ! Bring water at once and wash my feet. We are getting late. Take us across."

The ferryman brought a wood basin full of water. He washed Lord Rama's lotus feet with a heart over flowing with love. The gods in heaven envied his lot.

44. LORD RAMA CROSSING THE GANGA IN THE BOAT

Having washed the holy feet of Lord Rama, the boatman along with the other members of his family drank this nectar of his lotus-feet. This noble deed was instrumental in transporting the souls of his deceased forefathers to the heavenly abode.

Then the boatman gladly took the Lord across the Ganga. Getting down from the boat, Sita and Rama along with Guha and Lakshmana stood on the sands of the Ganga. The ferryman fell prostrate at Lord Rama's feet for his blessings. Sita took off her jewelled ring to give it to the boatman for his services. But he would not take it. He clung to Rama's feet and said, "O lord ! All my cravings have ceased to-day. Your glorious vision has ended all my sufferings and shortcomings."

45. BATHING IN THE GANGA

Having bathed in the holy Ganga, Rama worshipped a newly-made clay image of Lord Shiva. With Joined palms Sita addressed the celestial Ganga, "Mother, pray accomplish my desire, that I may return with my husband and his younger brother to purify our bodies with your holy waters once again."

The holy Ganga responded, "O Venerable Sita ! you shall safely return to Ayodhya with your beloved Lord and his younger brother Lakshmana. Every wish of your heart shall be fulfilled. The whole mankind shall worship you." Sita rejoiced to hear the blessings of goddess Ganga. Having invoked Ganesha and Shiva and bowing to the Ganga, they marched on.

46. IN THE HERMITAGE OF SAGE BHARDWAJ

When they reached the farther bank of the Ganga Rama spoke out, "Lakshmana, you are my sole armed guard now. You will be heading us. Sita will follow you and I shall walk behind you both so that Sita is well protected."

Next day having bathed in the holy confluence at Prayaga, they called on sage Bhardwaja who embraced Lord Rama to his bosom. The sage felt as if he had attained the bliss of oneness with Brahm or universal spirit. Rama inquired of him where they could live in peace and safety. The sage told them that Chitrakoot would be the most suitable place for them.

51

47. DASHRATHA BREAKS SEEING SUMANTRA ALONE

When Sumantra returned to the palace all alone, mother Kaushalya and father Dashratha were plunged into the ocean of grief. Kaushalya said to Sumantra, "Take me and leave me where Sita and Rama are. I too will live in the forest." Dashratha was more dead than alive. He said to Sumantra, "where is my Rama ? A son like him was never born in ages gone by and will never be born in times to come ! I am not worthy to be his father. I can't live without him. Take me where he is."

Dashratha's condition kept on worsening. All of a sudden he remembered the curse inflicted upon him by a blind sage long long ago. He spoke to Kaushalya to unburden his heart, "My dear ! No one can escape the fruit of his action. I happened to commit a horrible sin in my youth. Time has now come for that sin to be paid for with my life." Kaushalya requested the king to tell her the whole affair.

48. DASHRATHA NARRATED HOW HE KILLED SHRAVAN

Dashratha exclaimed, "When I was young, I had the skill to use my bow against unseen targets aiming by sound only. One night I went out in my chariot to hunt on the banks of the Sarayu. There was dense darkness. I waited for some wild animal to come. Suddenly I heard a gurgling sound as of an elephant drinking. I shot the arrow in the direction of the sound. But I was horrified to hear a human voice crying out in great pain. I hurried to the place to see that my arrow had pierced into the bosom of a young boy who lay in a pool of blood.

His name was Shravan." He cried, "O Sinner ! you have killed me. My old blind parents are thirsty at the hermitage. Take this pitcher of water to them. Do not tell them anything till they have quenched their thirst. This arrow is causing me a great pain. Pull it out."

"The moment I pulled out the arrow, Shravan looked at me and breathed his last. I stood trembling in every limb."

49. DASHRATHA BEGS FORGIVENESS OF BLIND PARENTS

Dashratha continued, "Dear Kaushalya, when I reached the hut with the pitcher of water, I saw that the old blind parents sat there like two birds with broken wings. I fell at their feet and confessed how in my ignorance I had killed their perfect son. The miserable parents were struck dumb by my dreadful tale. Tears poured down from their sightless eyes. I carried them to the river bank where their son lay dead. They burnt themselves alive in the funeral pyre of their son and cursed me that I too would die grieving for my son as they were dying.

"That curse is now haunting me. I can see the blind parents calling me to join them. My last moments are fast approaching."

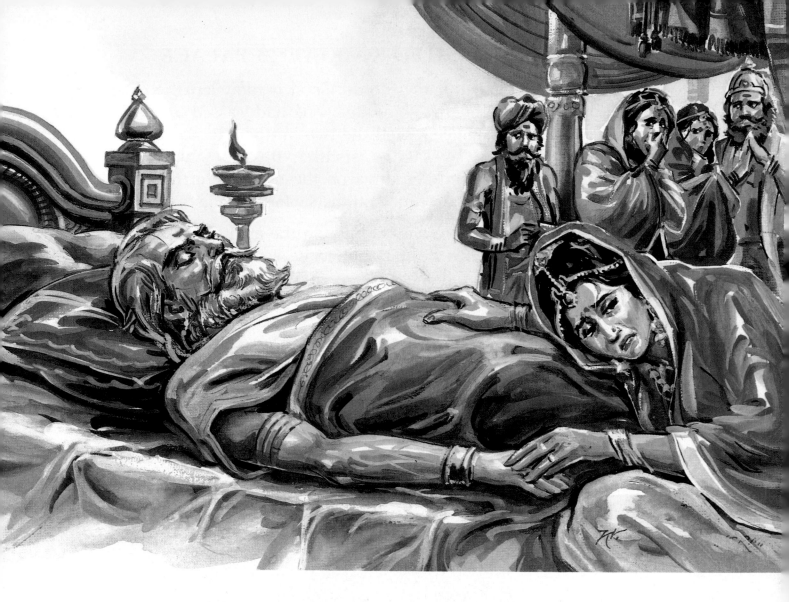

50. DASHRATHA BREATHED HIS LAST

Dashratha cried out, "Kaushalya ! I have gone blind like shravan's parents ! Yama's messengers are calling me. Will Rama come to save me from their clutches. Shall I see Rama before I die ? Yes, Rama alone can save me from Yama's messengers !"

After Rama's exile, Dashratha remained alive for only six days. So he uttered the name of Lord Rama six times before he breathed his last.

The whole palace plunged into gloom. All the queens were weeping bitterly. They clung to the body of the dead king praising him for his valour, virtues, name and fame. The servants wailed in deep anguish. There was weeping in every house in the whole city, "To-day has set the sun of the solar race who was the perfection of righteousness and piety."

When the day dawned the great and enlightened hermits arrived in the palace. Sage Vasishtha tried to disperse the gloom with the light of his wisdom. The king's dead body was immersed in a boat full of oil till Bharata's arrival. Fastest messengers were sent to fetch Bharata and Shatrughana.

51. BHARATA VISITED KAIKEYEE'S PALACE

All the secrets of nature are still unknown to us. Great is the telepathy of affection. Bharata had evil dreams at night that some dear one had passed away. His fears were confirmed when the messengers asked the two brothers to accompany them to Ayodhya at once as asked by sage Vasishtha. Bharata and Shatrughana mounted their chariots and reached Ayodhya on the morning of the eighth day. How long, difficult and slow was the journey on the swiftest of horses in those days !

The city wore a deserted look. There was sadness in the air itself. Bharata hurried to the palace to see his father but he was not to be seen anywhere. Then both the brothers entered Kaikeyee's palace. Kaikeyee jumped from her golden couch to embrace Bharata and Shatrughana.

52. MANTHRA KICKED HARD BY SHATRUGHANA

Both of them bent down and touched their mother's feet. Kaikeyee kissed their heads and welcomed them with maternal blessings.

Bharata said to her mother Kaikeyee, "Where is father ? I could not find him anywhere ? Where are Rama, Lakshaman and Sita ?

Kaikeyee spoke out with great power and pride, "My son, your father enjoyed life and all its blessings profusely. He attained great name and fame. He lived a virtuous life. He has now gone to his heavenly abode and joined the ranks of gods."

On hearing this the mighty Bharata fell to the ground and wept bitterly like an orphaned child in uncontrolled grief. Bharata then asked, "Mother, where is Rama ? Now he is both father and preceptor to me ! I must kiss his feet as he is now my sole refuge." When Kaikeyee told him that she had won the throne of Ayodhya for him by exiling Rama along with Sita and Lakshmana by virtue of her two boons, Bharata's grief knew no bounds. He burst out. "Murderess of your husband ! Greed blinded you. I cut myself off from all relation with you."

The moment Shatrughana saw wicked-hearted Manthra clad in her best, he kicked her so hard that her hunch and head were both broken.

53. BHARATA PERFORMING FUNERAL RITES

The great Vamadeva and Vasishtha consoled Bharata who was drowned in the ocean of grief. They said, "Dear son, have courage in your heart to perform the funeral rites of your great father." Bharata readily obeyed them. He had the king's body washed according to Vedic rites. A splendid funeral bier was prepared. Bharata clung to the feet of his mothers and prevented them from ascending the funeral pyre so that they could embrace Rama after his exile was over.

A sandal-wood pyre was raised in an artistic way on the banks of the Sarayu river. The earthly remains of the great Dashratha were consigned to the flames among Vedic chants. Then Bharata and others bathed in the Sarayu and offered water to the departed soul. Having performed all the funeral rites, Bharata gave away cows, horses, elephants and so many other gifts in charity to the holy and the poor.

54. LAKSHMANA ALARMED TO SEE BHARATA'S ARMY

Fourteen days after king Dashratha's death, the ministers called the Assembly. All spoke with one voice that Bharata should be crowned king. But Bharata said with folded hands, "It is my final decision not to accept the crown. All of us shall go to the forest. We will bring back Rama who alone shall be crowned king." All applauded Bharata's suggestion. What a devotion, perfection and renunciation on the part of Bharata !

The people of Ayodhya, saints and sages and the three mothers followed Bharata to the forest to fetch Rama. A huge army marched to protect them from wild animals. A vast cloud of dust covered the sky. Birds and beasts took to flight in Panic. Lakshmana climbed up a tall tree. He was alarmed to see Bharata with a huge army advancing towards their hut. He got ready to fight. But Rama told Lakshmana that Bharata was coming to take them back.

59

55. RAMA EMBRACES BHARATA

Halting the army at some distance, Bharata started forward with Shatrughana, Vasishtha and Sumantra. Soon they came to a cottage thatched with leaves near which stacks of faggots were heaped. On the walls of the cottage there were mighty bows and quivers full of deadly arrows. There were swords and other weapons of great excellence. It was after all a big question of self-defence in the dense forests and the annihilation of the demons. Bharata saw garments of bark spread out to dry on the branches of trees. These were the sure signs of Rama, Lakshmana and Sita dwelling there.

Then suddenly Bharata saw Rama himself seated with matted locks, a ruler of the world, with his mighty arms, breadth of chest and a face made to command love and obedience. By him sat Sita and Lakshmana. Rama's sight filled Bharata's heart with unbounded love. He sprang forward to the spot where Rama was seated. He could utter no word beyond "Brother", and fell at his feet sobbing. Bharata's tears washed Rama's holy feet.

Rama lifted Bharata with matted locks and in garments of bark and embraced him to his bosom. Gathering strength Bharata spoke, "Father could not bear separation from you. Uttering your name he has gone to his heavenly abode. I have come to crown you. Come with me and console your people who are without a king." When Rama heard his father's death he fell down like a tree felled by an axe. Bharata and Lakshmana along with Sita comforted him.

56. LORD RAMA OFFERS TARPAN

Rama and Lakshmana went to the Mandakini river to pour out libations (Tarpan) for their father's spirit.

Sage Vasishtha conducted the three queens to Rama's hut. There sat the four princes with faces clouded with sorrow. Seeing this, the royal mothers sank to the floor. The four brothers lifted them up. Rama reverently touched the feet of Vasishtha and sought his blessings.

Kaushalya embraced Sita and said, "My child, Janaka's daughter, daughter-in-law to the king of Ayodhya, do you live in this hut in the forest ? O, faded lotus flower ! O golden image covered with dust ! My heart melts to see you in such a miserable plight." Rama then turned to Bharata and exclaimed, "Dear brother, why have you given up your duties as a king ? Why have you clad yourself in deer skin. Why are these matted locks on your head ?"

57. BHARATA TAKING THE WOODEN SANDALS

All the Ministers, elders, sages, mothers and princes held an assembly outside the humble cottage of Rama. Bharata, the very embodiment of righteousness (Dharma) addressed Rama with folded hands, "All of us including the army have come to enthrone and crown you. With the departure of dear father to the heavens Ayodhya has become a widow without a rightful king. You alone can dispel the darkness from the kingdom. Do come with us, dear brother, to Ayodhya."

Rama replied, "Dear Bharata, I can never disobey father's word. Shatrughana is there to help you in ruling the land. If I fail to fulfil our father's wish I cannot find contentment even in the possession of the whole world. With Lakshmana by my side, I lack nothing. Brother, let us all four do our father's will." Bharata then spoke thus, "You are my father and my God. Your least wish is duty to me. Kindly give your wooden sandals that shall rule over Ayodhya till you return." "So be it," replied Rama. Bharata then turned back towards Ayodhya with all the people and the army.

(THE FOREST EPISODE)
58. VIRADHA SLAIN

After Bharata's departure to Ayodhya, Rama left Chitrakoota to visit the hermitage of sage Atri and his wife Anasooya. The sage embraced Rama and blessed him. The following morning, the three took leave of the sage and passed through a very dense forest infested with tigers and other wild animals. All of a sudden a huge man-eating demon Viradha like a broken hill pounced upon them. He picked up Sita like a toy. The two brothers pierced his whole body with their sharp shafts but he did not die. Then both of them thrashed him to death as weapons could not kill him.

59. RAMA MET SAGE AGASTYA

Then they proceeded towards the hermitage of sage Agastya who received them with utmost affection. The two brothers fell at his lotus-feet but the sage hugged them to his bosom. The sage said to Rama, "There is no other man so blessed as I am to-day. You are the very Fountain of Joy to all the saints and sages. Kindly dwell in my heart with your younger brother Lakshmana and the mistress of the three worlds Sita for ever." Rama bestowed the boon of eternal devotion on the sage.

Then the sage requested Rama, "If your mission is to free the earth from the burden of the demons, you should live at Panchavati." Rama bowed his head to Rishi Agastya and moved towards Panchavati with Lakshmana and Sita.

Sage Agastya was a man of great penance. He knew all the future course of events. So he gave Rama many divine weapons to kill the demons.

60. A HUT BUILT AT PANCHAVATI

Rama, Lakshmana and Sita lived peacefully among the saints and sages for about ten years. The hermitages of Rishies and Munies were free from the fears of the demons by virtue of the company of valiant Rama and Lakshmana.

But now on the advice of sage Agastya they had decided to live at Panchavati. On their way to Panchvati they saw a huge creature perched on a big tree. It was Jatayu, the devoted vulture who offered himself to protect Sita in the absence of Rama and Lakshmana. He happened to be a friend of Dashratha.

Rama was thrilled by the natural beauty of Panchavati. He asked Lakshmana to choose a good site and build a cottage there. First of all he raised the mud walls. Then the thatched roof was made. Rama admired the skill and swiftness of Lakshmana's workmanship. "Lakshmana, you are more than a father to me," said Rama shedding tears of love and joy. Indeed, Rama and Lakshmana are inseparable as Krishna and Arjuna. They are 'Nara' and Narayana, Jiva and Shiva. They seem to be separate because of ignorance. But they are one in two. Just see Lord Rama's love for his brother Lakshmana. He calls him a father and Lakshmana too considers Rama to be his father.

61. SHOORPANAKHA VISITED PANCHAVATI

Rama and Sita lived happily in the cottage at Panchavati. They were lovingly served by Lakshmana. One morning in early winter the three went as usual to the Godavari for their bath. Having offered oblations to their ancestors and prayers to the sun, Rama rose transfigured like Lord Shiva and returned to the cottage with Sita and Lakshmana.

The three sat outside their hut talking of spiritual wisdom, goodness and morality. Suddenly Ravana's sister shoorpanakha happened to come there. Her nails were as big as a winnowing fan. She was horribly ugly. But she could assume any lovely form at will. Seeing the divine beauty of Rama, lust and passion were aroused in her. Shoorpanakha said to Rama, "I fell in love with you at first sight. Now you are my husband !"

Later on she lost no time in deciding that Lakshmana could be a better husband than Rama as he was of a fair complexion. Infact, Shoorpanakha was a woman of loose character.

66

62. SHOORPANAKHA POUNCING UPON SITA

Rama told Shoorpanakha that he was already married. She should propose to his younger brother Lakshmana who was a bachelor. Lakshmana was equally handsome. So the lusty and passionate Shoorpanakha asked Lakshmana to marry her without any further delay.

Lakshmana exclaimed. "Fair lady ! He is befooling you. What is your status and what is mine ? I am a slave to my brother Rama while you are a princess. How can you be a slave's slave ? Ask Rama to take you as his second wife."

Now the sight of Sita enraged Shoorpanakha. She exclaimed to Rama, "It is this wretched little insect that stands between you and me. I will devour her in a trice." Uttering these words she sprang upon Sita.

Shoorpanakha possessed the ability to change her form according to her will. So she at once changed herself from a beautiful maiden to a horrible demoness who could devour Sita at one gulp. Sita was at her wit's end. She did not know how to protect herself from the advancing monster. Lord Rama saved Sita in the nick of time.

63. LAKSHMANA CHOPPING OFF HER NOSE

Sita screamed in fear. Rama intervened just in time to save Sita from the clutches of the horrible Shoorpanakha who had exposed herself as the ugliest demoness.

Rama then shouted to Lakshmana, "Look ! She deserves punishment. I have just been able to save Sita. Attend to this monster and teach her a lesson."

Lakshmana obeyed. He at once took up his sword and with great agility struck off her nose and ears, thereby inviting Ravana through her to a contest as it were. Without nose and ears she looked like a mountain flowing with torrents of red blood. Bleeding and mad with pain and rage, she flung herself before his brothers Khara and Dushana and exclaimed, "Fie, fie upon your manhood and strength, brothers !" Then she told them the whole story.

Shoorpanakha exclaimed, "Look at me, my brave brothers ! Rama and Lakshmana have committed such crimes on my person even though you are still alive. Moreover, they are dwelling fearlessly in your domain. And you while away your time here in pleasures of the flesh."

64. KHARA AND HIS ARMY LIQUIDATED

Khara, Dooshana and Trisara at the head of fourteen thousand demon soldiers came to avenge Shoorpnakha's mutilation. Rama asked Lakshmana to take Sita to a mountain cave for the sake of her safety.
Then Rama put on his armour and strung his bow. The Devas and Gandharvas hovered in the heavens to watch the battle. They showered their blessings on Rama.

The battle began. A constant stream of deadly arrows sped from Rama's bow named *Kodanda* in all directions before which the demon soldiers fell like moths before a blazing fire. Like rays from the sun, Rama's arrows brought down warriors, chariots, elephants and horses. Seeing Rama all alone fighting the demons numbered fourteen thousand, the gods and sages were alarmed. Then Lord Rama with his Cosmic Illusion wrought a great miracle. The demons saw one another in the form of Rama. So they fought among themselves and perished by themselves.

65. AKAMPANA APPRISED RAVANA

Sita and Lakshmana returned from the cave after the demon army had been exterminated. Lakshmana embraced Rama and rejoiced that single-handed he had given safety to the saints and sages dwelling in that Dandaka forest.

Akampana who had survived the horrible slaughter at the hands of Rama fled to Lanka in great terror to warn Ravana, the king of demons.

Ravana was furious with anger. He shouted at Akampana, "Who killed Khara, Dooshana, Trisara and my fourteen thousand soldiers ? Was it Yama or Agni or Vishnu ? I will deal death to the god of Death itself ! Speak out you coward !"

"Rama, son of Dashratha, who is lion-like in fierce valour killed all our great warriors single-handed ! The deadly arrows issuing from his bow like five-headed serpents pursued our soldiers wherever they ran and killed them. No one can compete with Rama's skill and speed in the use of weapons, "Akampana replied.

70

66. RAVANA VISITED MAREECHA

Akampana had been promised protection by Ravana. So he spoke fearlessly and frankly, "Listen to me, great king, no one including you can conquer Rama in a battle ! There is only one way of killing him. Rama's wife Sita is the most beautiful woman on this earth. Rama loves her more than his own life. Separation from Sita is sufficient to kill him. So manage to kidnap Sita !"

Ravana's lust for the beautiful Sita was aroused by Akampana. He went straight to Mareecha who was then leading a saintly life. Mareecha duly welcomed his king who told him, "Rama, the exiled prince of Ayodhya, has killed Khara, Dooshana, Trisara and a whole army of my men. I am resolved to kidnap his wife Sita. You help me in my designs."

Mareecha spoke out with folded hands, "To hanker after Rama's wife is the highway to disgrace, destruction and the annihilation of the whole demon race. Return to your devoted wives to enjoy your life and prosperity. Some enemy determined to destroy you must have advised you to carry off Sita to Lanka. If you carry Sita to Lanka, you, your relatives and your Lanka will surely go into the jaws of death and destruction." Hearing the sane advice of Mareecha, Ravana returned to Lanka.

67. SHOORPANAKHA REBUKED RAVANA

But Fate was going to conspire against Ravana as he had no equal in persecuting Devas, tormenting saints and sages and carrying away women by force. He had been a terror to all creatures. He feared neither God nor sin.

Ravana was seated on his throne when his sister Shoorpanakha bleeding and mutilated appeared before him. She was the vision of his doom. All looked at her with horror-struck eyes. She spoke in a bitter and biting tongue, "O slave of sensual pleasures, you are doomed to destruction and death ! Rama a mere man, has destroyed your outpost at Janasthana. When I tried to carry off Sita, Rama's matchless wife, for you, Lakshmana disfigured me thus. You must kidnap Sita to avenge my insult."

Ravana retired to muse alone. He thought again and again as Mareecha's words were ringing in his ears.

Ravana was no doubt a man of great learning. He was well-versed in the Vedas and the scriptures. But driven by greed, lust, anger and arrogance, he acted against his learning.

68. RAVANA AGAIN VISITED MAREECHA

Lured and fascinated by Sita's bewitching beauty as described by Akampana and Shoorpanakha, Ravana was driven to his impending doom. He mounted his flying chariot and landed at the hermitage of Mareecha who had turned a sage at the fag end of his life. He was amazed to see him a second time.

Ravana spoke out cleverly, "Mareecha ! you alone can save me from the trouble I am in. Our race has been disgraced. Sister Shoorpanakha has been disfigured by Lakshmana. Sages live fearless lives. Our great warriors and soldiers have been killed. I have decided to kidnap Sita from Panchavati. None on earth can equal you in courage, strength, skill and magical powers. Turn yourself into a golden deer with silver spots. Gambol in front of Sita near Rama's cottage. Sita will like to have your golden skin. She will send Rama and Lakshmana after you. When Sita is offguard, I will carry her off to Lanka in my flying chariot. If you refuse to carry out my plans, I will behead you with my sword this very moment." Mareecha shuddered and meekly obeyed Ravana.

73

69. RAMA CHASED THE DEER

Mareecha thought, "Ravana is doomed to die. Sinful desire is driving him to the abode of Yama. If I die at the hands of Rama, I will have my salvation and go to heaven."

Mareecha accompanied Ravana to the Dandaka forest where Rama lived in his humble hut. They alighted at some distance from the hut. Ravana took Mareecha by the hand. He directed him to the hut at Panchavati to carry out the plans as decided upon.

Mareecha at once tranformed himself into a wonderful golden deer. Every limb of the deer had a different hue. It charmed the eyes of the beholder like a rainbow in the sky. Its illusion was perfect like the mirage in the desert. Gold, silver, gems, flowers and diamonds appeared in quick succession on its charming skin.

This illusory deer of bewitching beauty wandered here, there and everywhere in the neighbourhood of Rama's hut. It would bend its head and nibble the grass on the earth. Sita was gathering flowers from the nearby shrubs that the deer caught her sight. She stood spell-bound staring at its wondrous skin. The deer stared back at Sita who wished to possess its beautiful skin.

Sita invited the attention of Rama and Lakshmana to the unique deer and said to them, "Do catch this deer for me alive or dead. Never before have I seen such a charming creature ! It is like a cluster of shining stars. Do go after it, my dear Lord !" Lakshmana took it to be a demon turned deer. But Rama had to yield to the wishes of Sita. He asked Lakshmana, "Be vigilant. Take care of Sita. Anything might happen at any moment." And Rama ran after the deer with bow and arrow in hands.

70. LAKSHMANA LEAVING THE HUT

Mareecha took Rama far out so that Ravana could get plenty of time and opportunity to kidnap Sita. Being tired of the pursuit, Rama bent his bow and sent forth an arrow which pierced the deer. Mareecha resumed his natural form and imitating Rama's voice called out, "Ah Sita, Ah Lakshmana !" before he fell dead. Hearing Rama's voice for help, Sita asked Lakshmana to run at once to help his brother.

Lakshmana feared some mishap. So before leaving the hut, he drew a holy demarcation line round the hut. He who dared cross it would get burnt to ashes.

71. RAVANA IN THE DISGUISE OF A SAINT

The moment Lakshmana left the hut, Ravana tranformed himself into a sage clad in saffron clothes. His lips were chanting Vedic hymns while his heart harboured ugliest evil.

Ravana was enslaved to see Sita's beauty. He asked for the alms. She came out of the hut as well as the demarcated line with some fruits and roots for the holy sage. Ravana caught hold of Sita and revealed his real identity. Sita was stunned. With one hand Ravana caught hold of her hair and with the other lifted her up to his chariot behind the trees and rose with her into the air. Hearing Sita's wails Jatayu fought against Ravana like a winged mountain.

72. THE GOLDEN DEER SLAIN BY RAMA

When the deer having been struck with Rama's arrow turned into Mareecha, Rama realized that the demon had duped them. Rama thought within himself, "It would be terrible if Lakshmana is also deceived by this imitated cry and leaves Sita alone to come to my help. The howling of jackals and behaviour of birds indicate some danger."

When Rama was hurrying back to the hut he ran into Lakshmana on the way. He held Lakshmana's hands and cried in sorrow, "Why did you desert Sita all alone in the hut ? She must be struggling for her life ! Lakshmana, we have lost Sita. If I do not see Sita in the hut on our return, I am bound to die. You alone will have to return to Ayodhya. How will mother bear this grief ? Why did you disobey me ? Lakshmana ! You must not have left Sita unguarded in the forest !"

Lakshmana answered with tears in his eyes, "Mother Sita charged me with evil designs and intentions when I told her that it was not your voice which was calling for help. But she was mad with fear and maddened me with her bitter remarks."

73. WOUNDED JATAYU

Rama wept and ran hither and thither to find out Sita. He asked the animals, birds and trees of the forest where Sita was. The two brothers searched for her on hills, by pools and on the river banks. But they failed to find her. Rama cried in great agony. His sorrow had swelled like the sea. Lakshmana tried to comfort him but all in vain.

As they walked on they were horrified to see Jatayu lying in a pool of blood on the ground. His whole body was wounded and mutilated beyond recognition. He was groaning with great pain.

Rama took Jatayu in his lap with great reverence and affection. The wounded bird spoke in a feeble voice, "Dear son ! Sita whom you are searching for has been carried off by Ravana. I tried to rescue her but the wicked demon cut off my wings with his sharp sword. I have clung to life to tell you what I know."

74. KABANDHA DELIVERED

Rama and Lakshmana moved from one place to another in search of Sita. When they reached the kronch Forest, a terrible demon caught hold of them.

In the twinkling of an eye the demon picked up Rama and Lakshmana with his hands like tiny toys. He was going to devour them into his huge mouth. Rama in a trice drew out his sharp sword and cut off both the hands of the demon. Having killed him they burnt him to ashes. Out of the fire emerged a charming man who said, "I am kabandha, the Gandharva. I had become a demon because of a curse which is now over. If you wish to discover Sita, make friends with Sugreeva, the ruler of the Vanaras." Uttering thus Kabandha rose up to his abode.

81

75. SHABRI'S SALVATION

Rama and Lakshmana now set forward towards Pampa as directed by Kabandha. Here in this beautiful region they visited the hermitage of aged Shabri, the disciple of famous sage Matanga who had told her that Rama, an incarnation of Vishnu, would bless her with His presence. Shabri's joy knew no bounds. She fed them with the most delicious fruits.

Lord Rama told Shabri that he loves a man or a woman of devotion the most. Even the greatest man of the earth lacking in devotion (Bhakti) is like a cloud without water. Devotion demands purity of mind and heart. Lord Rama exclaimed, "Blessed you are, O Shabri ! I have been drawn to you because you are as innocent as a child. You do deserve my Abode of Eternal bliss." Gazing on the glorious face of Lord Rama, Shabari having burnt her body in the fire of Yoga merged with the Supreme Brahm.

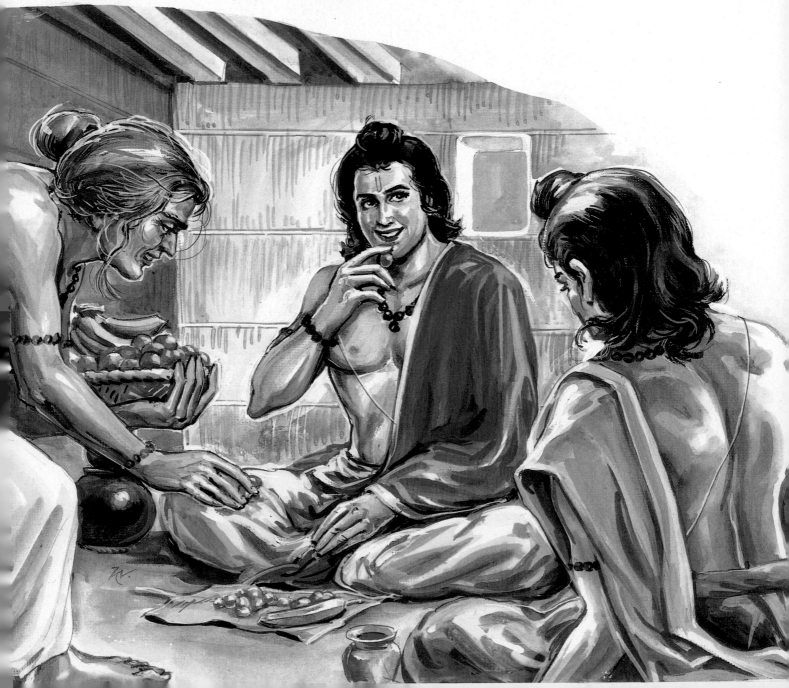

(THE KISHKINDHA EPISODE)
76. HANUMAN MEETING RAMA

Rama the incarnation of Vishnu had undertaken to suffer human sorrows gladly out of his own sweet will.

So searching and grieving for Sita, Rama and

Lakshmana marched ahead. Lakshmana tried to revive Rama's spirit, "Brother, too much love brings on grief and grief weakens effort. So be brave. Be hopeful."

When Rama and Lakshmana were wandering about Rishyamook mountain, the fugitive Vanara king Sugreeva was alarmed to see the two valiant youths. He suspected that his elder brother Vaali had sent those two warriors to kill him as he himself could not come there because of the curse of a sage. So Sugreeva asked Hanuman, his Chief Minister, to disguise himself as a Brahman to discover who they were.

He further advised Hanuman, "Be very careful lest you should get entrapped. Go, find out the truth and come back as soon as possible. Use all your wisdom and learning. I suspect their movements."

83

77. HANUMAN REVEALED HIMSELF

Having disguised himself as a Brahman, Hanuman went up to Rama and Lakshmana and bowing his head said to them, "Who are you young heroes roaming about in the woods dressed as both warriors and hermits at the same time ? Why do you tread the stony and thorny forest with your delicate lotus-like feet ? Do you belong to the Trinity ? Are you the twin divine sages Nara and Narayana ? Are you the Prime cause of the world ?"

"We are Rama and Lakshmana, sons of Emperor Dashratha of Kosala and have come to the forest to obey our father's command. We had with us Sita, daughter of King Janaka, who had been kidnapped by some demon. We are searching for her everywhere."

Having recognised his Lord, Hanuman fell at Rama's feet. Every pore of his body felt eternal bliss. Lord Shiva tells Parvati that bliss cannot be described in words. Hanuman then told Rama that Sugreeva, the Vanara king, had been deprived of his Kingdom and wife by his elder brother Vaali. Their friendship would do good to both of them.

Rama said to Hanuman, "You are an ideal messenger of your king. Infact, we were searching for Sugreeva and in you Sugreeva came searching us. What a lucky coincidence ! There is no doubt that our friendship with Sugreeva will prove to be a boon to him as well as to us."

78. HANUMAN LIFTED RAMA & LAKSHMANA ON HIS SHOULDERS

Hanuman, the crown of the learned, further exclaimed, "My Lord, my king Sugreeva will gain a lot by your friendship. It is now certain that he will regain both his wife and kingdom. The countless monkeys and bears at his command will certainly discover mother Sita wherever she might be."

Then the three decided to see Sugreeva at once. But the way up the mountain was too difficult for Rama and Lakshmana. It was meant for Vanaras only. So Hanuman resumed his natural form and carried Rama and Lakshmana on his back. His carrying the two brothers on his shoulders was an outward symbol of inward union. As friends and lovers embrace each other, Hanuman, the loving servant, rejoiced in carrying his Lord on his shoulders. Infact, Hanuman was born to serve Lord Rama.

When Sugreeva and his friends saw Hanuman flying to them with the two brave youths, they felt very happy to know them to be friends. Sugreeva and his men saw Hanuman coming with Rama & Lakshmana.

79. SUGREEVA & RAMA CONFER

Having made Rama and Lakshmana comfortable at Rishyamook mountain, Hanuman ascended the Malaya hill. He went in advance to Sugreeva and announced the visit of Rama and Lakshmana. He said to his King, "Rama is a prince of great wisdom, virtue and valour. His step-mother Kaikeyee forced his father king Dashratha to banish him for fourteen years. He came to the forest with his wife Sita and younger brother Lakshmana. They need your help to find out Sita who has been kidnapped in their absence by the demon king Ravana. Your friendship with them will enable you to get back your wife and kingdom from Vaali."

Sugreeva having assumed the form of a handsome man had a long heart-to-heart talk with Rama and Lakshmana. Rama accepted Sugreeva's hand of friendship and embraced him.

Sugreeva assured Rama, "My Lord ! You need not worry about Sita. I have millions of agile monkeys and bears at my disposal. I will send them in all the directions to trace out Sita."

80. FRIENDSHIP FORGED

Sugreeva narrated the story of his life to Rama. He told him that he was devoted to his elder brother, the mighty Vaali who also loved him a lot. But due to a great confusion in the killing of the demon Mayavi, the arrogant Vaali was bent upon killing him. He had already deprived him of his dear wife. The fear of Vaali had driven him to seek shelter on the Rishyamook mountain where Vaali would not come fearing the curse of sage Matanga.

Rama was shocked to hear the woeful tale of Sugreeva. He exclaimed, "Sugreeva, my dear friend, now grieve no more. I will serve your cause in every possible way. I will kill Vaali with a single arrow. Even Brahma and Shiva will not be able to save him from my arrow."

Rama further exclaimed, "One would incur great sin by the very sight of those who are not distressed to see the distress of a friend. A man should regard his own mountain-like troubles a mere grain of sand while the troubles of a friend should appear to him like Mount Sumeru even though they are as trifling as a grain of sand. A true friend loves his friend a hundred times more when he finds him in a crisis."

81. FRIENDSHIP CEMENTED

Then the learned Hanuman got together some faggots and kindled a fire. In the witness of the fire-god Rama and Sugreeva swore mutual friendship. They vowed, "Let our friendship be eternal. We will share our joys and sorrows."

Sugreeva showed Rama and Lakshmana some ornaments thrown from the sky by a weeping woman. Lakshmana exclaimed, "Indeed, these are Sita's anklets as I often saw them while worshipping her feet. But I am not familiar with the other jewels and ornaments as I never happened to look at mother Sita's face."

How full of loving reverence is this speech which sage Valmiki puts in the mouth of Lakshmana ! What a glorification of Lakshmana's character who was the very embodiment of virtue and valour.

82. SUGREEVA AND VAALI FIGHTING

Sugreeva was eager to regain his kingdom and family. Rama, Lakshmana and Sugreeva went to Kishkindha. Rama stood away behind a tree in a dense forest. Sugreeva challenged Vaali to a duel. The two brothers came out fighting fiercely to the dense forest where Rama stood ready behind a tree to kill Vaali.

But Rama was bewildered. He failed to differentiate Vaali from Sugreeva. The two brothers were so similar in form, features and method of fighting. Rama feared lest he should kill Sugreeva by mistake. So wounded and weary Sugreeva fled for life to the Rishyamook forest.

83. VAALI SLAIN

Rama consoled Sugreeva, "You and Vaali are alike in height, gait, shouts and in dress and ornaments. So I could not shoot my deadly arrow. Now have this garland round your neck for my recognition. Go now and challenge Vaali once again. I will surely slay him this time."

Sugreeva being satisfied, his spirits recovered. Evening was approaching. Sugreeva once again roared at the gate of Kishkindha. Vaali sprang stamping the earth in horrible rage. But his intelligent wife Tara holding him in a close embrace exclaimed, "My dear lord, give up this anger ! you have had enough fighting to-day. Fight to-morrow for you lack neither enemies nor valour. Sugreeva has befriended Rama and Lakshmana of unrivalled valour. Make it up with your brother and live in peace and prosperity."

But anger had clouded Vaali's intellect. Caught and dragged by the noose of death, he did not pay any heed to his wife's advice. The two brothers were soon engaged in a deadly duel. When Rama saw Sugreeva in trouble, he let go his deadly arrow which pierced Vaali's mighty chest. Vaali fell down in death's deep agony. He entrusted his son Angad and wife Tara to the care of Sugreeva and Rama before breathing his last.

84. HANUMAN TAKING RAMA'S RING

Sugreeva was crowned king and Angad was made the crown prince.

The rainy season set in. Sugreeva enjoyed power, pelf and luxury in his palace while Rama and Lakshmana spent the weary days waiting in a cave nearby. The forest paths were flooded. The end of the rainy season was awaited. The Raghu brothers were pining away in grief while Sugreeva was lost in luxuries.

Only Hanuman felt anxious about Rama's cause. Lakshmana and Hanuman aroused King Sugreeva from the slumber of his enjoyments. Sugreeva gave orders to his huge army that Sita must be discovered within a month. His army swarmed out like ants from an ant-hill and spread in the four directions with their leaders.

Rama gave his ring to Hanuman as he felt sure that he alone would discover Sita who would recognise him as his messenger on seeing his ring.

85. THE SEARCH BEGINS

The monkeys and bears fanned in all the directions. Hanuman, Angad and Jambavan travelled southwards.

All were eager and enthusiastic to catch and kill Ravana and redeem Sita. The armies that went North, East and West came back within a month to report that Sita was not be found anywhere. They had carefully searched forests, mountains, rivers and cities. But Hanuman had not yet returned from the South.

Hanuman and his party had travelled very far to the South in their search for Sita. Passing through a desert, fainting with hunger and thirst, they saw a cave from which birds were flying out full of joy. Having entered the cave, they were delighted to see trees laden with fruit and streams full of sweet water. There was a great city with golden palaces which were built by Maya, the architect of the demons.

There sat in a garden an ascetic woman named Swayamprabha who told Hanuman, as they were out to serve Lord Rama, to ask the monkeys to eat, drink and refresh themselves. No stranger who entered that cave could come out alive. But Swayamprabha out of love for Lord Rama transported all of them to the sea-shore by virtue of her Tapasya in a trice.

86. SAMPATI SPOTTED

Thanks to Swayamprabha all the monkeys and bears stood at the sea-shore. But the spring season had set in. The time limit set by Sugreeva to find out Sita had run out. If they now returned to Kishkindha without any clue about Sita, they would be put to death. So they decided to fast and seek death there and then.

From a neighbouring hill, Sampati, the vulture king saw a huge crowd of monkeys and bears willing to die. He had been famishing for a long time since his wings were burnt by the blazing sun. Now he was happy that he would get food for years without any effort. The monkeys praised Jatayu who died fighting against Ravana in order to save Sita. Hearing the name of his brother Jatayu, Sampati asked the monkeys to tell him the whole tale. Having heard the sacrifice of his brother Jatayu, tears welled up in his eyes. By virtue of his very keen eye-sight, Sampati told the monkeys that he could see Sita captive in Lanka ruled by Ravana. Many demonesses guarded Sita in the Ashoka garden of Lanka.

The Vanaras were delighted to get a clue about Sita. But the question before them was how to cross over the vast ocean lying before them in order to reach Lanka.

87. CONFERENCE TO CROSS THE SEA

The vanaras were delighted to know from Sampati that Sita was there in Lanka. Now they gave up their idea of fast unto death. But thought of the ways and means to cross the vast ocean.

They held a conference to discuss, "How can we cross the sea, enter Lanka, see Sita and return ?" Angad said, "Courage is the key to success. Never lose heart inspite of heavy odds. So dear warriors, tell me one by one, the longest jump you have the strength and courage to attempt."

Gaja could jump ten Yojanas, Gavaksha could jump twenty while a third claimed that he could do thirty. At last Jambavan, the oldest warrior, spoke, "I think I can manage to jump ninety Yojanas but Lanka is a hundredYojana far off. I regret my lost youth." The crown-prince Angad said, "I can jump a full hundred yojanas to reach Lanka. But the return journey might be hindered because of loss of strength in reaching Lanka."

Then Jambavan, the most experienced and aged warrior, cast his glance on Hanuman who sat apart in deep silence listening to everybody.

88. JAMBAVAN INSPIRING HANUMAN

Jambavan addressing Hanuman said, "I think that the son of wind god is the one best fitted by strength and skill to do this feat of jumping over the ocean."

Then he said to Hanuman, "O invincible warrior ! you are learned in all branches of knowledge. Why are you sitting silent and isolated ? You surpass all the rest of us in strength and wisdom. You are the equal of Rama and Lakshmana. If Garuda can cross the ocean, you too can easily cross it. But you are not aware of your prowess and valour. There is no equal to you in the whole world. You are unique, matchless and peerless. You are the mightiest and the most intelligent !"

Jambavan further exclaimed, "Anjana, your mother, was a goddess. She was born a Vanari by the curse of a sage. One day while she was wandering on a mountain, the wind-god fell in love with her and embraced her." The wind-god then remarked, "O Anjana ! A child will be born to you who will be equal to me in strength and vigour."

89. HANUMAN REMINDED DEVOURING THE SUN

Jambavana further reminded Hanuman, "When you were only a little child, you happened to look at the rising sun. You thought it to be a fruit to be eaten. So you flew towards the sun to pluck it. Seeing your spontaneous and effortless flight, Indra, the king of gods hurled his thunder bolt (Vajra) at you to protect the sun from your clutches. Your right jaw was broken and you fell down on a mountain. Your father, the wind-god, got enraged. He stopped his movements and stood still like a statue at one place. All living beings felt choked and strangled. Then all the gods asked pardon of your father and blessed you profusely. Brahma and Indra showered boons on you that no weapon can slay you. Death cannot come to you without your sweet will. You are immortal and imperishable, O son of Anjana and Wind-God !"

Jambavana continued, "O Hanuman ! you are equal to wind-god in splendour, intelligence and power. You are the beloved devotee of Lord Rama. You are the repository of all virtues. You are the foremost among the wise. You are the very fire which can consume the whole forest of the demon race. You possess a body shining as a mountain of gold. Immeasurable indeed is your strength." Hanuman was much delighted to hear the heartening speech of Jambavana.

90. HANUMAN WAS UP AND DOING

Jambavana continued to inspire Hanuman, "Inspite of possessing so much strength, you are virtuous and modest. You alone can fulfil Lord Rama's purpose. Crossing the sea is a child's play for you ! You can save all of us from sure death. Why do you leave your powers unused ? Arise, awake and stop not till the goal is reached ! Increase your stature. When in my youth I was as strong as you, I went round the globe twenty-one times. But now you are the only hope of all of us. O, noble son of Anjana, you inherit divine strength. Delay no longer. Realize your true nature and strength and spring forward to serve your Lord Rama whose blessings are ever with you. You can cross the ocean in a single jump."

91. HANUMAN FLIES

The dormant or sleeping powers of Hanuman were thus aroused by the aged and experienced Jambavana who was instrumental in reminding Maruti of his strength and potentialities which he had forgotten because of the curse of a sage. Hearing the inspirational sermons from Jambavana's mouth, Hanuman was back in his batting form. He began to swell like the sea in high tide. He assumed a Himalayan shape which could perform miracles in the twinkling of an eye. He kept on growing in size before the very eyes of the Vanaras who were overjoyed to see his enormous stature. The radiance that emanated from his body filled everybody with wonder, joy and hope.

Hence forward Hanuman is the hero of the Ramayana. He is called the 'Junior servant of Hari' by the devotees of Lord Vishnu. You know that Garuda is the 'Senior servant of Hari' as he is ever with Vishnu in flight. Inspired by Garuda Hanuman began to fly.

Now we shall see how Hanuman, the Junior Servant of Hari, ended the grief of Sita, destroyed by fire the citadel of the demons and returned to the Lord with the happiest news of Sita's discovery. Hanuman did what no one else could have done for his master.

(THE FASCINATING EPISODE)
92. HANUMAN ON HIS WAY TO LANKA

Reminded of his powers and potency by Jambavan, Hanuman was now bent upon to do anything for Rama's sake. With great zeal and fervour he uttered, "May your words become a reality. Undoubtedly without any hesitation I will fly over the ocean. No hurdle can stop me. I will land in Lanka and meet mother Sita. I will come back to you with good news. Let me press my foot hard against the earth to take the high jump. This hill can stand my weight."

Having uttered these words, Hanuman climbed up the Mahendra hill. Standing on the hill, he looked at the ocean and directed his mind concentrated in Yoga to Lanka. On his way to Lanka a mighty mountain rising up from the sea stood in his way. Hanuman struck it with his chest. It was Mynaka mountain who said, "My son ! Rest for a while so that you regain your strength to reach Lanka." Hanuman replied that he could not take even a moment's rest till he fulfilled his Lord's mission.

93. SURASA TRIED TO DEVOUR HANUMAN

The air roared as Hanuman sped fast in the sky. Beneath him his shadow travelled like a ship in the sea. It appeared as if a huge mountain with wings was flying in the sky. Hanuman possessed courage, foresight, and resolution. So he successfully overcame all hurdles on the way to Lanka.

Suddenly a huge form with its mouth wide open stood in Hanuman's way. It was Surasa, a mother of serpents, who had been sent by the gods to test Hanuman's wisdom and strength. She extended her mouth to a distance of eight miles to devour him. Hanuman at once grew double the size of her mouth. Then Surasa stretched her mouth to a circumference of a hundred and twenty-eight miles, the son of the wind-God immediately assumed a form covering two hundred and fifty-six miles. He kept on doubling the size of his body as compared to the size of her mouth. The moment Surasa expanded her mouth eight hundred miles wide, Hanuman reduced himself to a tiny form and came out of her mouth giving her a crushing defeat. Surasa gladly blessed him, "You shall fulfil Rama's mission. You are a treasure of strength and intelligence. I have gauged the extent of your wit and strength. The gods had sent me for this very purpose. The gods were not sure of your prowess. But I will now go and assure them that you possess many kinds of perfection. You have mastered eight kinds of Siddhies by virtue of which you expand and contract your body at will. You can become as heavy as a mountain and as light as the wind. You can display valour as none else can display. You possess matchless physical, intellectual and spiritual strength."

94. HANUMAN REACHES LANKA

Hanuman resumed his flight. There was a demoness who lived in the ocean. She used to catch the creatures flying in the sky by their reflection falling on the waters of the sea. Thus she devoured birds daily. This huge she-demon caught hold of Hanuman's shadow and dragged him down. She opened her cave-like mouth. Hanuman having entered her mouth ripped a way out through her stomach. The demoness died and sank down into the sea. Thus surviving many difficult trials, Hanuman flew across the sea. He had now approached the coast of Lanka covered with plantain and coconut trees. Hanuman climbed up a high hill to survey Lanka. It was a wonderful fortress with very high golden walls and enclosed by the ocean on all sides. A bird-eye view of Lanka situated on mount Trikoota revealed how beautiful, how wealthy and how well secured it was. Indra's Amaravati and Kubera's Alakapuri paled into insignificance before Ravana's splendour, wealth and military power.

After a great deal of thinking Hanuman decided to enter Lanka in the darkness of the night so that he could remain undetected. He reduced himself to the size of a little monkey as big as a cat. Having been blessed by Lankini, the Guardian goddess at the gate of Lanka, Hanuman climbed over the wall and jumped into the city in the darkness of the night. Soldiers and scouts were guarding the city everywhere. Hanuman searched mansion after mansion but Sita could not be seen anywhere. Then he entered Ravana's palace which was in every way a heaven on earth. Countless charming women lay sleeping in Ravana's spacious chamber, but there was no trace of Sita. With his spirit controlled by **Dharma,** Hanuman looked at all these sleeping women. Each was more beautiful than the other. They were all filled with joy and love. But none of them was Sita according to Hanuman's mind.

95. HANUMAN IN ASHOKA GARDEN

Hanuman felt dejected for a while as he could not see mother Sita anywhere in Lanka. Then he thought that Sita should not be there in that sensual paradise of happy damsels in Ravana's palace. He saw Ravana himself stretched, like another Mount Meru, on a golden bed studded with diamonds. Seeing his form and majestic splendour even Hanuman trembled for a moment. Coming out of Ravana's palace, Hanuman saw a park attached to a temple. It had high walls. Thinking that Sita must be there in that secluded Ashoka garden, Hanuman jumped over its walls and climbed up a high tree. As he looked below, he was delighted to see Sita under that very tree. She was blindingly beautiful and divinely pure. She was surrounded by so many she-demons.

96. RAVANA THREATENED SITA

The bright light of the moon enabled Hanuman to see Sita more closely. She was thin and pale. Her face was bathed in tears. Ugliest of she-demons were guarding Sita. They were swine-faced, tiger-faced, buffalo-faced and goat-faced. They were holding spears and other weapons in their hands to frighten Sita into Submission. Hanuman sat on the tree hidden in leaves.

It was still dark. The day had not yet dawned. Ravana was aroused from his slumber by the chanting of the Vedic Verses by his court bards. As soon as he awoke, Ravana clad in spotless white clothes started towards Ashoka garden to see Sita. He was surrounded by so many beautiful maidens. Ravana approached Sita to seek her love. He said, "O beautiful one ! I beg your love. Accept me to enjoy all the pleasures of the world. I will make you my sovereign consort. All my queens and women in my palace shall be ruled by you. Have pity on me. Be my wife. Only say 'yes'." Having plucked a blade of grass Sita spoke, "Deceitful Ravana, all your power and pelf are like this blade of grass to me. I think you to be a man of straw and a cowardly thief. Death stares you in the face. If you wish to live, seek forgiveness and safety at the feet of Lord Rama."

Ravana returned crestfallen.

97. HANUMAN TALKING TO SITA

Sita sobbed like a child when the horrible and ugly she-demons threatened to eat the limbs of her body.

A noble she-demon Trijata by name narrated her dream to all the other she-demons, "I saw Lanka in flames. Rama's monkey named Hanuman killed countless demons. Ravana riding naked on a donkey going to the abode of Death. Rama on his elephant carried Sita home." Hearing her dream all the she-demons were afraid and went to their homes.

Now Hanuman narrated in a sweet voice Rama's story from the beginning to the end. Sita was delighted to hear it. She asked the narrator to appear before her.

Hanuman stood before Sita with folded hands and said, "Mother, I am Hanuman, a messenger of Lord Rama. Here is Rama's ring for you. Do not grieve anymore. Very soon Rama and Lakshmana at the head of a huge and strong army of monkeys and bears would attack Lanka. Ravana and his

98. HANUMAN RUINED THE ASHOKA GARDEN

Having bowed low at the lotus-feet of mother Sita, Hanuman climbed up a tall tree. He bounced like a ball from one tree to another eating their sweet fruits and throwing down the unripe ones to the ground. Having satisfied his hunger, he uprooted many trees and destroyed the beautiful Ashoka garden. The demon guards were alarmed. Those who came to fight with him were sent to the abode of death by brave Hanuman. The guards who survived Hanuman's mace rushed to the court of Ravana and reported, "O king ! A huge monkey of terrible strength has ravaged the royal garden. He had a secret talk with Sita as well."

Ravana was furious to hear that the beautiful garden meant for his queens had been destroyed by a mere monkey. His eyes glowed like twin torches. He ordered his heroic son Aksha to go at the head of a huge army to capture the monkey. Seeing a huge army of demons coming towards him, Hanuman uprooted a huge tree and hurled it with a great force at the advancing army. Aksha and many other warriors were crushed to death under its terrible weight. The rest of the demons took to heels on seeing Yama in Hanuman.

Hearing that the prince had been killed by Hanuman, Ravana trembled with fear and rage. He called his son Indrajit and said to him, "You have mastered all weapons. None in the world can face you. Go and capture this monkey. Bring him to me."

99. INDRAJIT CAPTURES HANUMAN

Mounting in a chariot drawn by four fierce lions, Indrajit or Meghnath marched towards Hanuman twanging his bow-string. Hanuman roared and expanded the size of his body to a huge mountain. A terrible battle raged between the two warriors of equal skill and strength. All the arrows of Indrajit failed and proved to be an exercise in futility. Hanuman could not be defeated by any move of Meghnath.

Alarmed at Hanuman's strength and Stamina, Indrajit finding no way out to defeat him sent forth the Brahmastra as the last resort. At its touch Hanuman lay bound and helpless. He now remembered the boon he had secured from Brahma. Hanuman said to himself, "The Brahmastra can keep me bound for only one *Muhoorta* or four-fifths of an hour which comes to only forty-eight minutes. So there is no real risk. Let me see what the demons do to me while I lie bound."

The demon soldiers were still afraid of Hanuman. They thought that he was pretending helplessness. So they bound him hard with ropes of jute and coconut fibre. That very moment the supernatural weapon, the Brahmastra, withdrew its power because of the physical bonds of ropes which had defiled it. Now Hanuman could free himself at any moment as the supernatural weapon of Brahma could not be used a second time.

Hanuman felt happy in his heart as he could spring up free but he wished to see Ravana and talk to him. So he allowed himself to be dragged to the court of Ravana, the demon-king of Lanka. Women and children jeered at him. They were doomed to pay a heavy penalty for it as they had insulted a devotee of Lord Rama.

100. HANUMAN'S PREACHING TO RAVANA

Hanuman was presented before Ravana who sat on his golden throne clad in silk of golden colour. The whole court was brilliant with dazzling gold, gems, pearls and silk. Infact Ravana's greed for gold was insatiable. There were mountains of gold in Lanka, but Ravana was too greedy to give away even a single tola of gold in charity. Greed and lust were his greatest foes to spell his doom.

Ravana asked Hanuman, "Did Indra send you here ? Are you a servant of Kubera ? Speak the truth."

Hanuman replied, "I do not hail from Indra or Kubera. I am a messenger of Lord Rama and Chief Minister of Sugreeva, the king of the Vanaras. It was a cowardly act on your part to kidnap princess Sita to Lanka. Restore Sita to Lord Rama and ask his forgiveness. Be sure that Death has come to you in the form of Sita. Your boons will fail you. The entire demon race faces destruction if you do not seek refuge at Rama's feet. Heed my advice before it is too late."

Hearing Hanuman's preaching and warning, Ravana lost his temper and ordered that he should be killed forthwith. But Vibhishana observed that a messenger must not be killed. Ravana agreed to the advice given by his younger brother. He then ordered, "Set fire to his tail as a monkey loves his tail the most. Flog him hard and turn him out."

101. HANUMAN'S TAIL SET ABLAZE

Ravana's demon servants at once took Hanuman out. They wrapped his tail in rags of all kinds. Hanuman kept on elongating his tail and the demons kept on wrapping it with more and more old rags and pieces of cloth till not a piece of cloth was left in any house of Lanka. Then the longest of tails was dipped in oil and set ablaze like a huge flaming torch. Hanuman was taken through the streets of Lanka for the merriment of the people.

The women and children mocked at Hanuman saying, "Here goes the thief that entered our city. He will now be burnt to ashes."

When Sita in Ashoka garden heard about Hanuman's plight, she kindled a fire and prayed to the Fire god, "O Agni ! If I am virtuous and pure at heart, be cool to my son Hanuman. Do not hurt him in any way."

102. HANUMAN SET LANKA ON FIRE

Hanuman patiently endured the blows and the insults heaped upon him as he was taken from one street to another.

All of a sudden Hanuman shrank in size and shook off the ropes that bound him. In the twinkling of an eye he rose as high as a mountain. Then he jumped with his blazing tail to the top of a tall building reducing it to ashes. He plucked a huge pillar and threw it whirling in the air to cause terror in the hearts of demons. He jumped from house to house, setting fire to them. A strong wind began to blow with the result the whole city was enveloped in horrible flames.

103. LANKA REDUCED TO ASHES

Hanuman was so swift and rapid in his jumps that the whole city of Lanka was reduced to ashes in no time. Then he plunged into the sea to put out the fire in his tail. Sita's purity and her prayers had saved Hanuman from fire. Hanuman went straight to Sita who was delighted to see him safe and sound. He bowed low at her feet and said, "Oh mother ! Your power is immense ! Now allow me to go." Sita blessed Hanuman with all the powers at her disposal. When the monkeys waiting on the sea-shore saw Hanuman flying towards them they shouted in joy, "He is come ! Our saviour has come back from Lanka !"

104. HANUMAN TALKING TO RAMA.

All the Vanaras along with Hanuman, Angad and Jambavan flew towards Kishkindha to convey the message to their king Sugreeva and Lord Rama. They alighted near the protected park of Sugreeva and ate its fruit and drank honey to their fill. Dadhimukha, Sugreeva's uncle and keeper of the royal park, reported to Sugreeva who sat in the company of Rama and Lakshmana that his park had been destroyed by Angad, Hanuman and other monkeys returning from the South

Very soon the whole party arrived there. Hanuman fell at Lord Rama's feet and humbly said, "My Lord, with your grace I flew over the ocean to reach Lanka. I saw mother Sita chanting your name under the Ashoka tree in the royal garden. She is the very embodiment of purity and chastity. Ravana dare not touch her. She will live one month more to see you. Here is her **Sikha-mani**, crest-jewels, which she gave for you."

105. RAMA LOST IN SITA'S THOUGHTS

Rama further exclaimed, "Heroic son of God-wind, blessed are you who have seen Sita. I too see her now before me by virtue of your description. How shall I pay the debt I owe you ?"

Rama then retired into loneliness under a tree to ponder over ways and means to get back his beloved Sita. His mind wandered across the ocean to have a glimpse of Sita sitting pale and emaciated under the Ashoka tree in Ravana's garden. He could feel the agony and anguish of Sita's loneliness in the city of the demons. He wondered how she managed to survive. How she braved heat, cold and rain sitting under the tree surrounded by horrible-looking she-demons ! Rama wished he had wings to fly to Sita to embrace her in a trice.

But then he came to grapple with the reality of the situation. He got worried how his huge army would cross the vast ocean. If he failed to kill Ravana and his kiths and kins within a month, Sita might pine away in grief. So many diverse thoughts were troubling his mind. Rama now regained his lost composure. He was bubbling with optimism.

115

106. MONKEYS ON THE MARCH

Rama said to Sugreeva, "Hanuman has performed a miracle. He has preserved Sita's life by consoling her. He has saved my life also by bringing back good news about Sita. But, dear friend, how are we now going to cross the ocean ? Unless and until we reach Lanka there is no rescue for Sita".

Sugreeva said, "My Lord, be not dejected. Hanuman can carry you and Lakshmana on his shoulder to Lanka. All my warriors are ready to lay down their lives for you. If Hanuman can reach Lanka, we too shall certainly reach and conquer it. Now you order the armies to march to the sea-shore."

Lord Rama was born at noon. So his march at noon indicated his triumph.

The brave Vanaras carried Rama and Lakshmana on their shoulders so that the movement might be speedy. The army crossed mountains and forests rapidly and swiftly. At last they reached the sea-shore and camped in the forests near the sea.

107. DELIBERATIONS TO CROSS THE OCEAN

Having reached the sea-shore, there was a sudden halt for the rapidly advancing army of Lord Rama. Although every warrior and every soldier whether it happened to be a monkey or a bear was eager to reach Lanka yet the great barrier of the vast ocean stood in their way. Lord Rama was lost in deep thoughts. He was thinking of the ways and means by which that long stretch of water could be crossed.

Rama said to Sugreeva, "Dear friend ! I am simply bewildered. How our massive army is going to cross this broad, deep and mighty ocean ? What is the way out ? Think over it deeply and let me know."

All other warriors and commanders gathered together to join their heads in the deliberations. As soon as the moon rose, the waves began to leap up as if they were going to kiss the moon itself. But the mighty and mountain-high tides in the ocean could not dampen the spirits of Rama's army. They were full of hope and enthusiasm that the ocean would be crossed somehow or the other. And hope is life. Where there is a will, there is a way.

117

108. VIBHISHANA DESCENDED FROM THE SKY TO SEEK REFUGE

The demon-king Ravana was somewhat ashamed and afraid at the thought of what Hanuman, a mere monkey, had done in Lanka. He called a meeting of his ministers, warriors and commanders to chalk out the future course of action. All except Vibhishana proved to be flatterers and sycophants. They praised Ravana to the skies to bring about his downfall. But Vibhishana, Ravana's younger brother, spoke with folded hands, "Brother, what these people have said is sweet to hear but fatal to act upon. With Sita you have brought death for yourself and for your race. Unless you restore Sita to Rama, all of us shall certainly perish." Ravana was so angry to hear these words that he would have killed Vibhishana then and there if he had not been his brother.

Vibhishana along with his four noble friends at once rose up into the sky to seek refuge at the feet of Lord Rama. Sugreeva, the king and Commander of the Vanaras, suspected them of evil designs. But Rama said, "I cannot reject anyone who comes to me for protection."

109. RAMA PRAYING TO THE OCEAN

Sugreeva, Lakshmana and Vibhishana joined their heads together to devise the techniques of crossing the sea which lay before their army as the greatest hurdle. To start with they thought it best that Lord Rama should pray to the sea-god to give way to his army.

Rama was glad to accept their advice. He spread *Darbha* grass on the sea-shore and began his fast and prayers. He kept on fasting and praying to the sea-god for three days. But his prayers fell flat on the deaf ears of the ocean-god. Rama was now beside himself with rage. He got ready to dry up the ocean by his Agni-arrows.

110. THE SEA-GOD APPEARED

Taking his great bow Rama shot fiery arrows into the bosom of the sea. They were like the thunderbolts of Indra. The sea was disturbed to its depths. The sea creatures were in the grip of death and destruction as the tortured and heated waters began to exhale steam. It appeared as if Rama in his anger would convert the sea into a dry desert full of sands.

The Sea-god could stand it no longer. Shining like the rising sun and decked with jewels of gold, the Sea-god appeared in person and stood before Rama with folded hands.

The Sea-god said, "My Lord ! I am a slave to the eternal laws of nature. All the five elements like the earth, the air, the space, the fire and the water which go into the making of this universe have to abide by their very nature. None can deviate from its nature. I am by my very nature vast, deep, full of waves and impassable. But I will bear with your huge army. Let the monkeys bring boulders and trees to build a bridge over my bosom. In your army there is a great architect named Nala who is the son of Viswakarma. Let a path be built over me under his guidance so that your whole army crosses over me to Lanka."

The Sea-god then vanished bowing low to Rama.

111. THE OCEAN BRIDGED

Directed by Rama the leaders of monkeys sprang into the extensive forests in hundreds of thousands on every side. These leaders resembled mountains in size. They tore up rocks and huge trees and dragged them away to the sea. The colossal monkeys of extraordinary might filled the sea with rocks, boulders, hills and trees. Everybody was busy bringing something or the other from the forest according to his strength and capacity.

Within five days Nala with the help of countless monkeys built a bridge which was eighty miles wide and eight hundred miles long across the vast ocean. It looked as charming as the milky way in space. The gods, saints and sages showered their blessings upon the monkeys who were going to be instrumental in killing Ravana and his huge host.

112. RAVANA WITH RAMA'S ILLUSORY HEAD

Having reached the other shore by the bridge contructed by the great architect Nala, the army of monkeys encamped on the shores of Lanka which abounded in roots, fruits and drinking water. The moment Ravana heard that the sea had been bridged, the ten-headed monster exclaimed with all his ten tongues at once, "What ! Has Rama really bridged the waves, the billows, the sea, the ocean, the main, the deep, the brine, the tide, the hyaline, the lord of the rivers ?"

The lusty Ravana tried to win Sita'a heart by a magical illusion. He sent for a demon magician named Vidyut-Jihva (Lightning-Tongue) and ordered him, "Prepare a head which looks so exactly like Rama's that Sita thinks it is Rama's." Ravana showed Rama's illusory head to Sita who was horrified and wept bitterly.

123

113. RAVANA ATTACKED BY SUGREEVA

Ravana was somewhat terrified to hear that Rama's army had besieged Lanka from all sides. He went up the tower of his palace to witness Rama's army with his own eyes. He was horrified to see Lanka with its mountains, woods and forests besieged on all sides by countless monkeys who were eager to fight. Seeing the earth round about Lanka made brown by the huge army of monkeys, he became thoughtful as to how they were to be exterminated.

Sugreeva caught sight of Ravana watching his troops. His blood boiled on seeing the wicked demon who had kidnapped mother Sita. He sprang up into the sky and landed on top of the tower where Ravana stood. Sugreeva warned Ravana that it was his last day. Then he pounced upon him knocking off his crown and gave him a mighty blow. They wrestled together for a pretty long time. Both of them were mighty wrestlers. Ravana tried every move he had known in the art of wrestling. But he failed to overpower Sugreeva. Then he resorted to magic in place of wrestling. Sugreeva at once sprang back to where Rama was.

The monkey leaders showered praises on the son of the sun-god. Lord Rama was glad to see him safe and sound. What a valour Sugreeva had displayed ! Having observed bleeding wounds on his body, Lord Rama exclaimed, "Sugreeva ! I do wonder at your valour. But a king must not rush into risks of this kind." Sugreeva confessed his mistake.

114. ATTACK ON LANKA

Lord Rama could no longer tolerate that Sita should be a captive within the four walls of Lanka. So he ordered an immediate attack. The monkeys and bears rushed on the doomed city. They hurled huge boulders at the gates of the city. They threw gigantic trees at the demon soldiers crushing them to death under their heavy weight.

A huge army was sent out by Ravana in retaliation. A furious battle raged. The monkeys were merely armed with rocks and trees and used their nails and fists to tear apart the demons. Thousands fell dead on both the sides. Rama and Lakshmana killed thousands of demon soldiers with their sharp arrows. Blood flowed in streams.

115. INDRAJIT FELLED RAMA AND LAKSHMANA

The battle raged for the whole day. Even after sun-set the demons kept on fighting as their power increased a lot in the darkness of the night.

There was terrible slaughter on either side. Angad fought a duel with Indrajit, Ravana's most valiant son who had conquered Indra himself. He killed his horses and charioteer smashing the chariot to pieces of wood. Hanuman was engaged in a duel with Jambumali and Neela fought against Nikumbha, Kumbhakarana's brave son.

Now Indrajit who was rendered helpless by Angad resorted to magic and sorcery. He made himself invisible. Then he aimed arrows at Rama and Lakshmana as from nowhere. The two brothers looked here, there and everywhere, but Indrajit could not be seen anywhere. Even then deadly missiles were being showered on them continuously. They were simply puzzled and bewildered.

Indrajit then decided to shoot serpent arrows at Rama and Lakshmana. He bound both the brothers with these arrows. They fell on the battlefield in a swoon. All the monkeys were plunged in the ocean of grief. Nobody knew what to do. There was a great panic in Rama's camp.

116. RAMA REGAINING CONSCIOUSNESS

Ravana was beside himself with joy when Indrajit returned victorious from the battlefield. He told his father that he had killed both Rama and Lakshmana. Sita was taken in the *Pushpaka Vimana* to the battlefield where she saw Rama and Lakshmana lying motionless on the earth. Her grief knew no bounds. But Trijata consoled her that both of them were alive but in a swoon.

As the force of the arrows charged with magic and sorcery weakened, Rama sat up and held Lakshmana in his lap. Sugreeva asked his uncle Sushena how dear Lakshmana could be revived. That very moment the sea and the air were churned up by a gust of mighty wind out of which appeared the great bird Garuda of Lord Vishnu. At the very sight of dreaded Garuda the serpent darts vanished. Rama and Lakshmana both stood up, healthier and stronger than before. A wave of joy ran through the monkeys.

117. THE BATTLE RESUMED

There were noisy rejoicings among the Vanaras who got ready once again to launch a massive attack on the fortress of Lanka by the orders of Lord Rama and Sugreeva. Some demon guards rushed to Ravana and exclaimed, "Great king ! Rama and Lakshmana have regained life. They are raging about the battlefield like hungry lions. Indrajit's arrows proved to be an exercise in futility."

Ravana was dumb-founded. His face fell. Filled with great anxiety he said, "I fail to understand what you say. No one has ever escaped these arrows of Indrajit. He who has rendered these arrows powerless is not an ordinary man. We are in danger now."

Red with rage Ravana ordered Dhoomraksha to go and kill the two little men. But he was killed by Hanuman. Ravana was now beside himself with rage and grief.

Seated in his radiant chariot, the ten-headed Ravana appeared on the battlefield like a Rudra, the destroyer. A great battle ensued. Blood began to flow in streams. Ravana could not be defeated by either Neela or Hanuman. He caused great destruction. Lakshmana was felled into a swoon by Ravana (*Then Rama rode on Hanuman's shoulders to give battle to Ravana. He wounded him badly. Ravana's golden crown, his chariot and weapons were broken. Taking pity on him, Rama asked Ravana to go away to take rest for the day*).

118. RAVANA'S CHARIOT SMASHED

Rama saw the majestic and glowing frame of Ravana with great interest and pity. He exclaimed, "Ravana is no doubt a great warrior. But he is too wicked to deserve any pity. He must be killed."

Then Rama came forward to give battle to Ravana. The sharp arrows that issued forth from his great bow wounded Ravana badly. His golden crown was broken. His chariot was smashed to pieces. He stood helpless on the ground without any weapon at all. He was fatigued and tired. His wounds were bleeding.

Lord Rama took pity on helpless Ravana. He said to him, "you have fought bravely. You seem to be tired. Go home to rest. Come back to-morrow to fight with new weapons."

Ravana retreated with great shame to Lanka.

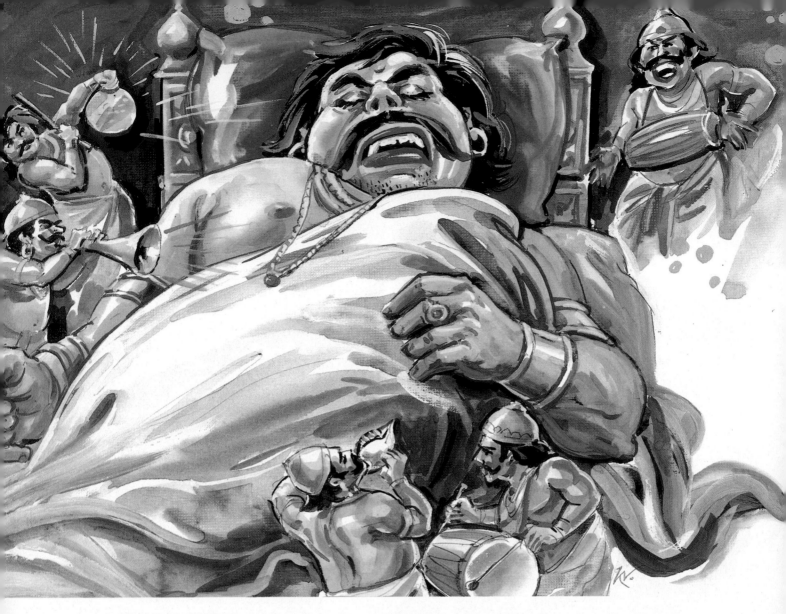

119. KUMBHAKARANA AROUSED FROM SLUMBER

When Ravana returned humbled and dejected from the battlefield by virtue of the mercy shown to him by Lord Rama, the gods rejoiced at the imminent end of the demon king. For a while he fell into a great depression and dejection. But then having gathered courage and confidence, Ravana ordered that Kumbhakarana be aroused from his slumber at once.

He had gone into slumber only nine days ago. So it was a difficult task to arouse him. Drums were beaten violently and conches were blown loudly close to his ears. But the giant did not stir at all. Then the elephants were made to walk on his body. He opened his eyes, sat up and began to eat and drink. He ate heaps of meat and drank hundreds of pots of blood and wine kept ready for him by his elder brother Ravana. Then he went to Ravana and exclaimed, "Great brother, tell me who wants to die at my hands ? Why have you aroused me ? Ravana replied, "While you were lost in sleep, Rama has caused great destruction."

Kumbhakarana said, "Driven by lust you have ruined yourself. But worry not. I am going to kill Rama and Lakshmana right now."

120. KUMBHAKARANA SLAIN

Kumbhakarana armed with his huge spear marched to the battle-field all alone. But Ravana sent an army to help him.

Kumbhakarana was tall and mighty-limbed. He was a giant even among the demons. As he stepped out of the gates of Lanka, the monkeys were terror-stricken on seeing his huge and vast body like a mountain. Frightened they fled in all directions. It was with great difficulty that their chiefs called them back to the battlefield.

Angad and Sugreeva were struck down by the mighty Kumbhakarana who picked up unconscious Sugreeva to carry him to Lanka. But Sugreeva revived on the way. He bit with his teeth and tore with his nails the ears and nose of Kumbhakarana who in pain threw him down. He at once flew to Rama's camp. None could stop Kumbhakarana from killing and devouring the monkeys. Rama with his sharp arrows cut off his legs. But legless he rushed forward on his stumps. Then Rama cut off his head with his sharp and swift shaft which carried it to Lanka where it fell like a huge red hill. Hearing Kumbhakarana's fall Ravana felt as if he himself had died. He fell into a swoon.

121. THE VANARAS EMBOLDENED

When Ravana recovered from his swoon, he groaned in grief, "Ah mighty brother ! My right hand is no more ! How Rama could kill you ? The gods rejoice in your death. The monkeys and bears are dancing in delight. How can I live without you, O my departed brother ? How stupid of me ! Perhaps Rama is Vishnu himself !"

Ravana in Lanka moaned in grief and despair. But there was great and hilarious jubilation in Rama's camps. All the monkeys were on their feet. They were up and doing and full of great fervour and enthusiasm. They fell upon the demon soldiers with renewed strength and stamina. Now they had become absolutely fearless as the giant Khumbhakarana was no more to plague and pester them.

The demon army took to its heels under the massive attack of the Vanaras. But thousands of them were sent to the abode of Death.

The mighty monkeys were bewildered to see something incredible to their eyes in the distance. All eyes were directed towards a chariot coming towards them. Indrajit was seated in it with an illusory image of Sita. But the monkeys took it to be real Sita.

The monkeys were shocked to see Indrajit catching hold of Sita in a wicked and barbarous way. He waved his long sword in the air. He warned the monkey warriors to stand where they were. If they came closer to his chariot and tried to attack him, he would behead Sita with his sword. The monkeys stood dazed.

122. INDRAJIT WITH ILLUSORY SITA

Indrajit was a master of hallucination and illusion. He created an illusory image of Sita. Having seated her in his chariot he drove her to the battlefield in the midst of monkeys. He drew out his sword and seemingly killed her in the presence of the Vanaras. Deceived and horrified the monkeys ran to Rama and Lakshmana and conveyed to them the heart-rending news of Sita's slaughter before their very eyes. Everyone was plunged into the ocean of grief. But Vibhishana who knew Indrajit very well told Rama and Lakshmana that it was merely a trick of magic and sorcery. Indrajit was trying to defeat them through magic. All heaved a sigh of relief. Vibhishana further told Lord Rama that his special spies had brought the news that Indrajit through this trick of killing Sita wanted to gain time to perform a Yajna.

123. INDRAJIT HURLS BRAHMASTRA

Indrajit then went to Lanka to comfort his grieving father Ravana. He exclaimed, "Dear father ! you need not worry at all as long as I am alive. I am more than sufficient to destroy Rama's whole army. To-day neither Rama nor Lakshmana shall see the setting sun." With a huge army at his disposal Indrajit launched a massive attack on Rama's army. Seeking Rama's permission and accompanied by Angada and Hanuman, Lakshmana marched forth in great fury with bow and arrow in hands. Lakshmana and Meghnada grappled with each other in mounting fury. Neither could get the better of the other. Then Meghanada resorted to unfair means.

Lakshmana growing furious smashed his chariot to pieces and killed the charioteer. The demon was all but dead. Indrajit thought that Lakshmana would not spare him that day. So as a last resort he pierced Lakshmana's bosom with the invincible Brahmastra. Lakshmana fell into a swoon.

124. HANUMAN WITH SANJEEVANI

There was an atmosphere of great gloom and grief in Rama's camp because of Lakshmana's swoon. Rama put Lakshmana's head in his lap and wept bitterly. Jambavan, the bull among the bears, inquired if Hanuman was alive. Hanuman bowed low at his feet. Jambavan exclaimed, "Dear son ! Fly northwards at once across the sea to the high Himalayas. There is the Hill of rare Herbs between the Rishabha and the Kailash peaks. Four shining herbs illuminate the ten directions. One of those herbs is Mritsanjivani which can restore the dead to life. Taking it, you ought to come back with all speed before the sun rises."

Hanuman fell at Lord Rama's feet and sought his blessings. He flew straight towards the Himalayas like the wind-god. He crossed all hurdles on the way including the demon Kalnemi whom he killed. He reached the Kailash peak and recognised the resplendent Hill of Herbs. Uprooting it and lifting it on his palm, Hanuman flew back at a terrific speed without losing even a single moment.

125. BHARATA STRIKES HANUMAN

Holding up the Hill of Herbs on his hand, Hanuman darted back through the air. It was still night. Bharata used to keep vigil at night ever since his return from Chitrakoota. He saw Hanuman flying over Ayodhya with a huge mountain. Thinking him to be a demon, Bharata drew his bow to the ear and struck Hanuman down with a headless arrow. Struck by the arrow, Hanuman dropped unconscious to the ground crying, "Rama ! Rama !" Bharata was ashamed of himself as in haste he had struck down a devotee of Lord Rama. He rushed to the spot where Hanuman had fallen. He revived him by uttering the name of Lord Rama ceaselessly.

Realizing his blunder Bharata embraced Hanuman to his bosom. He told him the whole tale very briefly. Bharata asked Hanuman to ascend his arrow to reach in time. But he flew back himself well before sun-rise. As soon as Mritsanjivani was administered to Lakshmana, he got up with renewed vigour and enthusiasm. Lord Rama hugged Lakshmana to his bosom. His joy knew no bounds. The whole host of bears and monkeys surrounded Lakshmana with their beaming faces.

126. INDRAJIT PERFORMING YAJNA

The moment Lakshmana got up from his swoon, he asked, "Where is Indrajit ? Has he again fled to hide himself in the clouds ? I will kill him. Great was the joy in Rama's heart and the bears and monkeys danced in jubilation. Having hugged Lakshmana to his bosom, Rama told him how he had been struck down by Indrajit into a swoon.

Meanwhile Indrajit was performing a demoniac sacrifice to become invincible. Lakshmana accompanied by Vibhishana, Hanuman and other warriors went to the spot in the mountains where Indrajit was about to offer oblations to evil spirits. The monkeys defiled the sacrifice. A long and fierce battle was fought between Lakshmana and Indrajit.

127. INDRAJIT SLAIN

Indrajit's chariot was destroyed. Both the heroes stood on the ground. At last Lakshmana chanted the *Indra-astra* spell and uttering Rama's name shot the fatal arrow. Indrajit's head was cut off and fell to the ground. The Devas showered flowers from the heavens as their conqueror was no more.

Lakshmana was wounded all over and bleeding. Rama embraced him warmly.

Ravana had been deprived of his right hand by the death of his most valiant son Indrajit. He was so much dejected that he thought of killing Sita who was the root cause of all his misfortunes. Ravana cried in rage, "It is best to kill Sita who is the root cause of all this tragedy. My son Indrajit killed the Illusory Sita. Let me kill real Sita who has wrought the destruction of my entire family." So saying he rushed out with a sword in his hand. But his wise Minister Suparsva appealed to his better sense, "Great king ! How dare you think such a lowly thought. How can you incur the shame and sin of killing a woman ? You are the master of the Vedas and all other sciences. Direct your anger against Rama." Ravana changed his mind.

128. RAVANA ON BATTLEFIELD

He had no choice but to march to the battlefield. He seated in his chariot which was as swift as the wind. Many demons who were matchless in strength accompanied him. Numberless ill-omens occurred at that time. But the arrogant Ravana was not to be cowed down. Frightful jackals, vultures and donkeys gave a shrill cry while dogs whined in large numbers.

Ravana caused great havoc on the battlefield by discharging sharp and powerful arrows from his bow in all directions. Hanuman with his powerful mace looked like Yama himself killing thousands of demon soldiers. The gigantic monkeys and bears rushed forward like hosts of winged mountains of different colours. With claws and teeth, rocks and huge trees, they despatched the demons to the abode of Yama. Rama bent his bow and sent showers of arrows against the demons in all directions. He was destroying the demon soldiers like a raging fire. Although the warriors could see their companions fall yet they could not see Rama because of the constant shower of arrows.

129. GREAT DEMONS SLAIN

Many great demon warriors were engaged in combats and duels with Hanuman, Angad, Sugreeva and a host of others. There were Kumbha and Nikumbha who were the two mighty sons of the great monster Khumbhakarana. Yoopaksha, Mahodara, Mahaparswa, Virupaksa and the like were all peerless and matchless in their valour and strength. Kumbha was slain by Sugreeva and Nikumbha fell a prey to Hanuman whose mighty fist could be seen everywhere on the battle-field sending the demons to death and destruction.

The day belonged to Sugreeva who knocked down the most powerful demons like Virupaksa and Mahodara. He struck a violent blow with his palm on Virupaksa's temple. It worked like a thunderbolt. The demon fell to the ground emitting blood from all the nine apertures of his body.

130. RAMA FACES RAVANA

Then he firmly seized hold of a huge rock and hurled it at Mahodara who shattered it to thousand pieces by his arrows. Sugreeva then snatched Mahodara's sword and beheaded him in a trice.

When all the great warriors of Ravana including his sons, brothers, kiths and kins were killed in the battle he himself came to the front to meet his doom. He was a broken man after his peerless son Indrajit had been killed by Lakshmana. Then he addressed his commanders for the first time with folded hands, "Kindly kill Rama with all your strength. If you fail, I will kill him. "Adversity had made him mild of tongue. Now that his commanders lay dead on the field, he had come out to face Rama and Lakshmana himself.

Rama along with Vibhishana went ahead to face the ten-headed monster who showered a spate of arrows mounted on his swiftest chariot. Vibhishana asked Lord Rama in wonder how bare-footed without a chariot and armour, he would defeat the mighty Ravana.

Lord Rama described the victory chariot, "Valour and fortitude are its wheels. Truthfulness and virtuous conduct are its banner and standard. Strength, discretion, self-control and benevolence are its four horses. Forgiveness, compassion and evenness of mind are its reins. Adoration of God is the charioteer. Dispassion is the shield and contentment is the sword of the chariot of victory. Charity is the axe. Reason is the fierce lance and the highest wisdom is the relentless bow of the chariot of victory. A pure and steady mind is like a quiver. Quietude and the various forms of abstinence (Yamas) and religious observances (Niyamas) are a sheaf of arrows. Homage to the Brahmans and to one's own preceptor is an impenetrable coat of mail. Dear Vibhishana, he who possesses such a chariot of piety and righteousness shall have no enemy to conquer anywhere." Rama already possessed all these virtues. So he was fearless.

131. RAMA AND LAKSHMANA IN CHARIOT

But the selfish gods in the Heaven wished to see Rama victorious at any cost so that their troubles were over without anymore delay. So Indra, the Lord of heaven, sent his own chariot with Matali, the charioteer, driven by four high-spirited and charming horses. These horses knew no decay or death. They could fly as swiftly as the mind or thought of man.

The monkeys rushed forward with renewed vigour and enthusiasm when they saw Rama and Lakshmana mounted on the most wonderful chariot.

The powerful monkey warriors looked like the god of death in fury. Crushing the champions of the demon host they roared like thunder clouds.

132. RAVANA'S FALL

Mounted on his divine chariot driven by eight horses and filled with all kinds of weapons, Ravana came roaring to the battlefield.

He flooded the battlefield with arrows shot in all directions Now he was face to face with Rama who rendered all the arrows of Ravana futile.

Matali, Indra's charioteer, whispered into Rama's ear, "May I remind you of Brahma-astra which alone can kill this demon-king ?"

Having uttered the spell Rama shot the Brahma-astra which pierced Ravana's chest. The nectar in his naval got dried up. The great monster fell down dead uttering for the first time, "Hai Rama." Lord Rama sent him to his heavenly abode.

133. VIBHISHANA CROWNED

The gods blew their trumpets in heavens at the fall of Ravana and showered flowers on victorious Rama.

Vibhishana burst into weeping when he saw his dead brother lying in the dust on the battlefield. Rama consoled Vibhishana saying, "Ravana fought like a true hero. Death has washed all his sins. He has gone to Heaven. You need not mourn for him." Then Rama asked Vibhishana to perform the funeral rites of his departed brother. Having performed the last rites, Vibhishana came back to Lord Rama and bowed low at his lotus-feet. Lakshmana was sent to Lanka along with Sugreeva, Angad, Nala, Neela, Jambavana and Hanuman for the coronation ceremony of Vibhishana. With due reverence Vibhishana was seated on the throne of Lanka and Lakshmana applied the Tilak of kingship on his forehead and crowned him king amidst gaiety and grandeur. They glorified him. Nay, joining their palms, they all bowed their heads to him. Then with king Vibhishana they returned to Lord Rama who was overjoyed to see the crown of Lanka on his friend's head.

134. RAMA SENDING FOR SITA

Rama said to Hanuman, "Seeking Vibhishana's permission, go to Ashoka Vatika and convey to Sita the news of our victory over Ravana."

Sita's joy was beyond words. Hanuman wished to kill the she-demons who had troubled her so much. But Sita said, "No my son ! None is blameless in this world. Noble souls show compassion even to their foes !" Generations of pious men treasure these words of mother Sita like nectar itself.

Rama then ordered Vibhishana to bring Sita in a palanquin. The monkeys were all eager to see mother Sita. Rama asked Sita to come on foot. Sita alighted from the palanquin and advanced towards Rama with downcast eyes. Rama's face darkened. He spoke harshly to Sita, "It gives me no joy to get you back unless you satisfy me and others by passing through a fiery ordeal to prove your purity." Infact, Lord Rama was omniscient. He had already requested Sita to enter fire before she was kidnapped by Ravana. Now he was merely asking the shadow of Sita to be burnt in fire so that real Sita could come out of fire where it had been lodged. This secret was not known to anybody except the eternal couple.

135. SITA'S FIERY ORDEAL

Sita bowed to Lord Rama's command as she was pure in thought, word and deed. She said to Lakshmana, "Go and fetch the faggots to kindle a fire for me." Lakshmana with tears in his eyes obeyed mother Sita and kindled a big fire. Sita rejoiced at heart to see the blazing fire. She went round her Lord Rama thrice and exclaimed, "ye Gods ! I bow to you. Oh Saints and sages I bow at your holy feet. Oh Fire-god you are a witness to my purity ! If I have sinned even in my dream, burn me to ashes."

Having uttered these words, Sita jumped into the leaping flames. A wonder of wonders was witnessed ! All the gods had assembled in the flames of fire. First of all Brahma spoke with folded hands, "Vishnu ! did you not take human form to kill Ravana ? Is Sita not your own Lakshmi ?" Agni, the Fire-god, lifted Sita in his arms and presented her to Rama with great reverence.

Rama joyfully accepted her eternal consort Sita. Just as Shiv and Shakti are one and the same, Ram and Rama are one. Sita is Lord Rama's power (Shakti) which is the source of all delight in this universe. But the two are inseparable.

136. RAMA EXPLAINS

Rama requested Sita not to take to heart what he had asked her to do. He consoled her by telling her that he was already convinced of her purity and chastity without any doubt at all. He for himself needed no proof at all about it. But the people of the world had to be convinced and satisfied lest they should resort to mud-slinging at his beloved queen later on.

Then the soul of Emperor Dashratha descended from the Heaven to bless Rama, Lakshmana and Sita. It said to Rama, "Supreme joy is being experienced by me to-day on seeing you hale and hearty and satisfied in mind as you have exterminated all your enemies in the period of your exile. I have been redeemed by you, my worthy and high-souled son."

Then Dashratha addressed Sita, "My child ! Forgive my son Rama for the wrong he did you to preserve the Dharma and ways of world."

Rama with joined palms prayed to his father, "Kindly be gracious to Kaikeyee and Bharata. You said to Kaikayee, 'I disown you with your son Bharata.' May this terrible curse not fall on mother Kaikeyee and brother Bharata." "Let it be so !" said Dashratha. Here in lies the greatness of Lord Rama who is worshipped even to-day and will be worshipped till eternity.

137. RAMA LEAVING FOR AYODHYA

Dashratha's soul having returned to heaven the mighty Indra stood before Rama with folded hands saying, "O Rama ! You are a jewel among human beings. All the gods are extremely pleased with you for freeing this world from the menace of the demons. Pray, speak out your wish." Rama exclaimed, "Bring back to life all the monkeys and bears that died fighting for me on the battlefield so that they get reunited with their near and dear ones, O Indra, the great." "Be it so !" said Indra. All the monkeys who were alive were amazed and overjoyed to see their dead friends rising up from their long slumber. What a love Rama displayed !

Rama's heart went out to Bharata who had been waiting for him in Ayodhya as an ascetic of great penance for full fourteen years. Sita, Rama, Lakshmana, the monkey warriors and Vibhishana boarded the Pushpaka aeroplane which could expand and contract according to need. Now they were in the air flying speedily to Ayodhya. As they flew in the sky Rama invited Sita's attention to the bridge built by Nala and the monkeys. Sita had a bird eye view of Kishkindha where Rama forged friendship with Hanuman and Sugreeva. Alighting at sage Bhardwaj's hermitage, Rama sent word in advance to Guha and Bharata. Then the most sacred city of Ayodhya came in view. The gracious Rama and Sita both bowed their heads low to Ayodhya.

At the sight of his dear motherland Ayodhya tears of love rushed to Lord Rama's eyes. Every hair on his body stood erect and he felt delighted again and again and then he said to Sita and Lakshmana, "Mother and motherland are dearer to me than heaven itself."

138. RAMA EMBRACING BHARATA

Hanuman had gone ahead to tell Bharata the news of Rama's arrival. In a moment the natives of Ayodhya heard that dear Rama was coming. They decorated the whole city like a bride. The moment Rama saw the great sages Vamadeva and Vasishtha ahead of all the people ready to welcome him, he dropped his bow and arrows on the ground and ran with brother Lakshmana to clasp his preceptor's lotus feet. Sage Vasishtha embraced them and inquired after their welfare. Then Bharata fell on Rama's lotus feet which are adored by gods and sages as well as by Lord Shiva and Brahma. He lay prostrate on the ground and would not rise even though being lifted up. Then the all-merciful Rama forcibly lifted him up and pressed Bharata to his broad bosom. Every hair on his swarthy body stood erect and his lotus eyes were flooded with tears of boundless love.

139. RAMA'S CORONATION

Sage Vasishtha called the learned Brahmans and said to them, "The day and the hour and all other factors are favourable for Shri Ramachandra to occupy the royal throne. His coronation shall bring delight to the whole human race." All of them were delighted to hear his auspicious words.

With Guru's permission Rama disentangled his matted hair and bathed himself. Then he dressed and decked himself with jewels. The beauty of his person put to shame hundreds of Cupids. The mothers-in-law immediately bathed sita and attired her in heavenly robes and precious jewels. Rama and Sita were seated on the heavenly throne. The sages were overjoyed. The learned Brahmans recited the Vedic hymns. The gods in the heavens above shouted, "Victory ! victory !!" Sage Vasishtha first of all applied the sacred Tilak on Rama's forehead and put the glorious crown on his head. Then all the sages blessed Rama from the core of their hearts. The mothers were transported with joy at the sight of their son on the throne. They gave away gifts to the Brahmans. The mothers gave the beggars so much that they begged no more.

(THE UTTARA EPISODE)
140. HANUMAN'S HEART

One day six months after his coronation Rama called all the monkeys and his friends and said to them, "All of you are dearer to me than my life. But now return to your homes." Rich gifts soaked in love were showered lavishly upon them and Rama saw them off with his blessings.

Hanuman wished to stay back to serve Rama's lotus feet. Taunted by Sugreeva, Hanuman with Rama's name on his lips tore off his chest with his nails. Sugreeva was wonder-struck to see Rama and Sita seated on the throne of Hanuman's heart. He at once freed him from all bonds.

143. RAMA ORDERING LAKSHMANA

Rama was plunged in the ocean of grief at this latest report. He looked crestfallen. He spoke to the door-keeper seated nearby, "Bring immediately Lakshmana, Bharata and the unconquered Satrughana."

His brothers having arrived, King Rama addressed them thus, "O guardians of the people ! you constitute all my possessions. You are my very life. I am simply looking after the kingdom carved out by you. You have practised the teachings of the scriptures. You have a mature intellect. This problem of mine deserves to be pondered over by you all together."

All the three brothers were shaken within when king Rama spoke in a depressed tone. King Rama further exclaimed, "Dear brothers ! The glory of our ancestors is as glorious as the sun itself. I accepted Sita as the fire-god declared that she was free from sins. My inner conscience even now bears testimony to her purity and nobility. But the citizens of Ayodhya speak ill of her day and night. They complain that their wives may also go astray and live for sometime with other men and then come back home. If I fail to satisfy my people, I am dead as a king. O Lakshmana ! To-morrow morning take Sita in Sumantra's chariot and leave her on the other side of the Ganga near the hermitage of sage Valmiki. Do what I say without asking anything." King Rama further said to Lakshmana, "Any resistance on your part will cause me extreme displeasure. Tell Sita that you are taking her on a pilgrimage as many a time she had expressed her desire to visit the hermitage of saints."

144. SITA EXILED

As the night passed away grief-stricken Lakshmana spoke to Sumantra, "O charioteer, yoke the speedy horses to the best chariot and equip it with a splendid seat for Sita as ordered by King Ramachandra. Sita has to be taken to the hermitage of the pious sages."

Having seated Sita in the chariot, the horses moved speedily towards the Ganga. Sita saw ill-omens in abundance. She was terrified.

reached the other bank of the Ganga, Lakshmana exclaimed with folded My heart is pierced with a mighty arrow ! You have been forsaken by the king afraid of the ill-report about you circulating among the citizens. Dwell in the hermitage of sage Valmiki who is a friend of my father Dashratha." Sita fell into a swoon for sometime.

158

145. LAKSHMANA COMING BACK

Recovering from the swoon, Sita spoke to Lakshmana thus, "This mortal frame of mine was indeed created by the creator for sorrow. So to-day I am the very embodiment of sorrow. What sin has been committed by me ? I cannot give up my life by drowning myself in the waters of the Ganga as the descendant of my Lord Rama to be born from my womb will perish. O son of Sumantra ! Do as you are ordered to do. Forsake me the misearble one, to my fate ! Tell my Lord to bear himself in such a way that the ill-report among the citizens is proved to be wrong. His task is dearer to me than my own life. May God bless you, O Lakshmana."

Lakshmana went round Sita with tears streaming from his eyes and spoke thus, "O auspicious one. O faultless one, your beauty is not seen by me as your feet alone were the object of my vision till now. Oh ! how shall I have your vision now ?"

Lakshmana once again touched Sita's lotus feet and turned his back upon her. With a heavy heart full of great remorse, he sped back to Ayodhya in the empty chariot. Sita cried in wilderness surrounded by peacocks.

146. VALMIKI SEES SITA

The young sons of the hermits who lived in the hermitage of sage Valmiki saw Sita sobbing bitterly. They ran to the great sage and exclaimed, "A noble lady having the appearance of the Goddess of wealth is weeping loudly in despair near the bank of the river. Her looks are really divine ! Kindly give her shelter."

Hearing their words Valmiki the foremost of sages, knew everything by virtue of his asceticism. He rapidly stepped towards Sita and spoke to her thus, "You are the daughter-in-law of Dashratha and the beloved queen of Rama and also the daughter of King Janaka. Welcome to you, O one loyal to your husband ! O fortunate one your purity is known to me. All that exists in the three worlds is known to me. Yes, indeed, with my inner eye acquired through penance, I have seen that you are absolutely sinless. O child ! the female ascetics in my hermitage shall always look after you as their child. Accept this offering. Be calm and free from all maladies. You are entering your home."

Sita felt consoled and followed the great sage to his hermitage where the ladies received her with great affection of a mother.

147. LAVA AND KUSHA BORN

Shatrughana on his way to kill the demon Lavana stayed for a night at the hermitage of Valmiki. That very night Sita gave birth to two sons. At mid-night the young ascetics spoke to sage Valmiki about the auspicious motherhood of Sita. The sage was delighted to hear it. Valmiki approached to see the two sons who were as effulgent as the new moon. Then he made the protection symbol that would destroy the evil spirits of the nether world. Taking a handful of Kusha Valmiki said to the old women attending on Sita, "He who was born first should be cleansed with the Kusas (upper portion of the grass) purified by chants and he will be named 'Kusha'. He who is born, afterwards should be cleaned carefully with Lava (lower portion of the grass) and he will be known by the name of 'Lava'."

Noble Shatrughana heard at midnight the joyful Gotra and name of Shri Rama and also the news of delivery of the two sons by Sita. He was beside himself with joy. At break of dawn, having performed the morning duties, he took leave of the sage with folded hands and resumed his journey. There was a great merriment in the hermitage of sage Valmiki who could see beforehand what was going to happen in the future. Now his great Epic the Ramayana was going to be completed. He began writing the 'Lava-Kusha episode' with great eagerness. He was in a blissful state as his penance had fructified in the birth of Lava and Kusha. Their horoscopes revealed that they would be victorious in battle. They would grow up to be modest, accomplished and handsome. They were the very images of Lord Rama.

148. VALMIKI TRAINING TWINS

Kusha and Lava were fortunate enough to be brought up in the lap of nature under the protection and guidance of the great sage Valmiki. Both of them revered their Guru Valmiki and mother Sita from the core of their hearts. As they grew up, Valmiki began imparting them education suited to their age and stature.

The two brothers would recite in a sweet voice the story of Rama and Sita, the Ramayana, which was written by their revered Guru Valmiki himself.

Valmiki trained the two brothers in the art and craft of archery. They became perfect bowmen with the passage of time. At a very young age, they knew and practised much more than what was possessed by old warriors of great repute as the sage gave them all he had.

149. HORSE SACRIFICE YAJNA

Lord Rama wished to perform the Asvamedha Yajna. He spoke to Lakshmana, "Let all the sages including Vasishtha, Vamadeva, Jabali, Kasyapa be brought together along with all the Brahmans so that I may let loose a horse after consulting all of them."

Sage Vasishtha asked Bharata, Lakshmana and Satrughana to make all the preparations for the horse-sacrifice Yajna. Then Lord Rama sent his messengers in all directions to fetch the kings, saints, and sages who were to take part in that grand Yajna. All the great kings along with Jamavana, Sugreeva, Vibhishana, Nala, Neela, Vardhana and Kubera came to participate in the sacrifice. Thousands of disciples accompanied the illustrious sage Vishwamitra. King Janaka also graced the occasion with his presence.

A beautiful golden statue of Sita was placed to the left of king Ramachandra as no holy sacrifice could be performed without the presence of the wife. The Yajna started with the chants of Vedic hymns. A white steed of rare breed stood there bedecked with precious jewels and ornaments.

150. PREPARATIONS FOR THE YAJNA

The great sacrificial place had been prepared in the Naimisa forest on the banks of the Gomati by Virtue of its being extremely holy. One lakh carriages and carts carried foodgrains to the place of sacrifice. Bharata was ordered to carry many hundred millions of gold and silver coins carefully in advance. Many rows of mobile markets, actors, dancers, cooks damsels possessed of eternal charm accompanied Bharata. Many costly dwellings for the powerful kings were built.

As long as Rama lived at Naimisa, all the kings brought presents for him. They were duly honoured. Food and drinks, clothes and all other requirements were provided for them. In that grand sacrifice only one direction was heard, "Go on distributing till the needy ones are satisfied."

He who desired wealth got it. He who desired jewels got them. A heap of silver, gold, gems and garments being distributed constantly was seen in that sacrifice for more than a year. Sages who were rich in penance exclaimed that such a sacrifice was never performed before by Indra, Soma, Yama and Varuna ! There was no one unclean, poor or emaciated in that best horse-sacrifice of Lord Rama who was surrounded by happy and well-nourished people. The aged and noble ascetics who came there were all praise for the grand Yajna the like of which they had never seen before in their whole life so far.

151. HORSE RELEASING CEREMONY

The Yajna having been completed, the white steed was brought near the sacred fire. King Ramachandra applied a glorious Tilak on its forehead. A declaration was hung round its neck. "This horse belongs to Koshala Emperor Ramachandra, the exterminator of his foes. He who captures this horse shall have to wage a war with him. Those who accept his lordship shall have to pay taxes imposed by him."

Satrughana, the killer of foes, followed the horse at the head of a strong army.

152. LAVA KUSHA CATCH THE HORSE

Satrughana was advised not to trouble any innocent person on the way. Many petty kings bowed before Satrughana and his horse. They gladly agreed to pay yearly tribute to Emperor Shri Ramachandra. Then the horse happened to pass through a dense forest where the hermitage of sage Valmiki was situated.

The twin brothers Lava and Kusha were fascinated to see the gait of the beautiful white horse passing by their hut. They caught hold of it and tied it to a tree. When they read the declaration round its neck, they eagerly waited for its defenders to face them.

153. FIGHTING RAMA'S SOLDIERS

Their wait ended soon after king Rama's soldiers arrived there tracing the hoofs of the horse. They flew into a rage on seeing the horse tied to a tree. But when they saw two hermit boys of tender age guarding the horse, they cooled down a bit. The soldiers asked them to let go the horse. The brothers asked in amazement, "Why ? We are not illiterate. We have already read the declaration of your king. Get ready for a battle if you want the horse otherwise go your way leaving the horse to us."

The soldiers once again tried their best to persuade the two brothers with great affection to free the horse. But they were too obstinate to do it. Flying into a rage, they aimed their arrows at Lava and Kusha.

The twins retaliated with a mighty twang of their bows shooting down a number of soldiers. Those who survived took to their heels fearing the two young warriors. The fugitive soldiers narrated their sordid tale to Satrughana who was simply amazed to hear their narration. He consoled them amd accompanied them to the spot where the horse was tied.

154. SHATRUGHANA DEFEATED

No sooner did Shatrughana see the two brothers of a very young age than a fountain of fatherly love spontaneously gurgled forth in his heart. He exclaimed, "Charming children ! This horse is not a toy to play with. I will give you wonderful toys. I shall be very thankful to you if you only let go this horse of ours."

Then the two brothers asked him, "O king ! who are you ? Which is your kingdom ? Why do you wander about these deserted forests with your army ? Have you lost something which you wish to discover ? Why have you let loose this horse ? Do you wish to conquer the whole earth ? Then, first of all conquer us."

Shatrughana was stunned to hear a spate of questions from the young hermits. However, he told them everything regarding the purpose of the horse sacrifice. "Are you then afraid of fighting ?" asked the twins.

Shatrughana was enraged. He picked up his bow and arrow. Lava and Kusa like lightning shot sharp shafts which broke Shatrughana's chariot. Now Shatrughana was bent upon waging a war. He ordered the soldiers, "Capture these two boys. Snatch the horse from them. If you fail in your attempt to redeem the horse, let me know. I shall then face them myself."

As the army came into action, Lava and Kusha with their divine arrows deprived the soldiers of their weapons. Now they dared not face the twins. They took to heels in great panic.

155. SHATRUGHANA BOUND

Shatrughana's rage knew no bounds when he helplessly saw his chariot being broken to pieces before his very eyes and that too by two young children. In his violent anger he forgot that he was facing affectionate children.

Now he showered a volley of powerful arrows aimed at Kusha and Lava. Perhaps he was not pretty sure of his own prowess. So he ordered his soldiers to join him in the fight so that the horse could be freed from the clutches of the two valiant brothers.

A terrible battle was waged. Both the brothers were dead shots. They never missed their targets. After all they were the disciples of sage Valmiki who could see every incident before it actually occurred. The people of Ayodhya had to be taught a lesson. Pride does have a fall sooner or later. So the great Rishi Valmiki had prepared Lava and Kusha to face any exigency with glorious success.

Soon the two brothers destroyed the whole army. Shatrughana's every limb was wounded so badly that he fell down on the ground in a swoon. The surviving soldiers fled to Lord Rama and told him what havoc had been caused by two young sons of a hermit.

Rama then ordered Lakshmana to go and see what the matter was. He advised him not to kill the two hermit boys. They should be captured alive.

Lakshmana was at his wits' end. He failed to understand how the two young hermit boys succeeded in giving a crushing defeat to Shatrughana, the slayer of foes.

(LAVA-KUSHA EPISODE)
156. LAKSHMANA FACES NEPHEWS

The moment Lakshmana saw the two lovable faces facing him, he requested them to be good enough to return the horse without any more of fighting. But the two brothers mocked at him.

In a playful mood Kusha aimed an arrow at Lakshmana's beautiful crown which went flying into the air and fell with a thud at a long distance. Lakshmana was cut to the quick.

157. KUSHA IN A SWOON

Seeing the crown flying off his head, enraged Lakshmana shot powerful arrows at the two brothers. But Lava and Kusha parried all his arrows without any problem at all. After the battle of the arrows, Kusha launched a mighty blow at Lakshmana which he failed to edure. His mind accepted defeat at the hands of the young warriors. It was really a miracle to Lakshmana.

He remembered Lord Rama in his distress and then aimed a mighty arrow at Kusha who was wounded and fell into a swoon. Lava was grief-stricken. Having put down his bow and arrows on the ground, he meditated on his great Guru Valmiki by whose grace Kusha got up with a start. He congratulated Lakshmana as he seemed to be a warrior.

Lava and Kusha then rendered all the arrows of Lakshmana futile. Then Lava put on his bow the invincible arrow given to him by sage Valmiki and let it go at Lakshmana who fell down senseless.

158. BHARATA CALLED

Rama's army was routed as soon as Lakshmana fell into a swoon on the battlefield. The soldiers terrified at the bravery of the twins fled the field. They told their king that the young warriors could not be defeated. Lakshmana lay unconscious on the field.

Lord Rama then sent for Bharata who stood before him with folded hands. Having heard patiently what Rama ordained him, Bharata seeking his pardon spoke thus, "Great king ! I think Sita's curse is causing all this havoc. Never before have we suffered such an ignoble defeat !"

Lord Rama assuming a grim posture retorted, "Bharata ! Are you afraid of fighting ? If so, order my army to get ready. I will go to give a battle myself to these erring sons of the hermits."

Bharata felt ashamed of himself at such bitter remarks by Lord Rama. He sought his pardon and prepared himself to go to the battlefield.

We know that Bharata was deeply devoted and dedicated to Lord Rama. He could never think of going against his Lord's will even in the dream. Generally people are interested in acquiring the Four Fruits of Life—Dharma (righteousness), Artha (wealth), Kama (fulfilment of desires) and Moksha (salvation). But Bharata did not attach any importance to these Four Fruits.

159. RAMA RECALLING BHARATA

Lord Rama was greatly perturbed and puzzled in his mind. He was afraid lest Bharata should also lick the dust. So he recalled him to tell that he should ask Hanuman and his Vanara warriors to accompany him. Bharata said to himself, "I fail to understand how Lakshmana, the slayer of Meghnada, failed to defeat the two lads. Some supernatural curse has been inflicted upon our king who has banished innocent Sita for no fault."

160. BHARATA ORDERS HANUMAN

As per Rama's bidding Bharata first of all sent for Hanuman. Then he said to him, "Dear friend Hanuman ! you gather together all the monkey warriors to give battle to the sons of the ascetic. I too get ready in the mean time."

Hanuman engaged himself in the task of collecting his warriors. Very soon he was accompanied with Jambavana, Sugreeva, Mayand, Angad, Nala and Neela, the greatest of warrriors among his tribe. Then he informed of his readiness to Bharata.

Having come out of his palace Bharata advanced to the battlefield at the head of his army of monkeys who had been instrumental in vanquishing the demon-king Ravana. The warriors who had conquered Lanka accompanied Bharata. There were Jambavana, Sugreeva, Mayand, Angad, Nala and Neela who had struck terror in the hearts of the demons.

But now the conditions were entirely different. They were to face ascetic boys of great penance who were the very embodiments of valour and innocence. How could Sage Valmiki be humbled ?

161. BHARATA STRIKES LAVA

Lava and Kusha were overjoyed to see the monkey army coming to the battlefield. They knew that Rama had been victorious by the valour of the Vanaras.

The Vanaras were welcomed with sharp arrows by Lava and Kusha. Most of them were now licking the dust. Hanuman was all praise to the two young warriors.

Bharata could not decide what to do as he looked on the innocent faces of the two children. When Hanuman failed to tackle the twins, Bharata lost his temper. He shot from his bow a very powerful arrow at Lava who reeled to the ground under its impact. Seeing his brother falling into a swoon, Kusha's rage knew no bounds.He set an arrow to his bow and having chanted some spell shot it with great force into Bharata's chest. Bharata could not bear its impact and fell to the ground senseless. All the monkey warriors were wonder-struck to see Bharata falling to the ground by the force of Kusha's arrow. They consulted Hanuman and Sugreeva. But they too were at their wit's end. Hanuman could see with his intellectual eyes that Lava and Kusha were the sons of Lord Rama and mother Sita.

162. RAMA FACES SONS

As soon as Kusha pulled out the arrow of Lava's body, he regained consciousness. When Lord Rama got the news of the defeat of the Vanara army as well as Bharata in a swoon on the battlefield, he was deeply grieved.

Having gathered his army he marched to the battlefield himself accompanied by Vibhishana. Hardly had the Lord glanced at Lava and Kusha when he felt spellbound by their charm. He lovingly called them to his side and exclaimed, "Dear children ! Who are you ? Who are your parents ? You are truly the very embodiment of bravery that you have won such a great battle by your own valour !"

The twins replied, "Don't entangle us in your sweet talks. You may hear all about us in heaven !"

163. LAVA KUSHA FACE FATHER

Lord Rama insisted that they must tell him everything about themselves before the battle could be resumed.

The twins spoke thus, "My name is Kusha and he is Lava, my younger brother. Our mother is the revered daughter of the great King Janaka of Mithila. We have been brought up by sage Valmiki. But we do not know the name or the dynasty of our father whom we never saw before."

Lord Rama's joy knew no bounds as he stood face to face with his own glorious sons who were really as resplendent as the sun god himself.

Then the twins challenged Lord Rama, "O great King ! Either fight or leave the horse in our custody and flee the field as we do not attack a runaway warrior.

Smiling Lord Rama picked up his bow. He parried the arrows hurled at him by Lava Kusha but he himself did not shoot even a single arrow at them. Rama's soldiers failed to understand Lord Rama's behaviour. Lava said to Kusha, "Dear brother, I fail to understand the tactics of King Rama. We are raining arrows at him. But he is not retaliating. He is simply defending himself against our arrows. Why is it so ?" Kusha replied that he too was puzzled at his tactics.

164. HANUMAN BOUND

When Hanuman saw that his Lord was not attacking the twins at all, he got enraged. He came into the arena with his mace. Seeing Hanuman meddling without any rhyme or reason, Kusha too lost his temper. There ensued a duel between Hanuman and Kusha.

In a trice Kusha was able to overpower Hanuman. He tied both his hands and feet with a rope.

Then Kusha spoke to Lava, "Dear brother, we shall carry this monkey to mother who will be delighted to see him."

Then the twins carried Hanuman to their hermitage.

165. SITA SEES HANUMAN

Having left Hanuman outside their cottage, Lava and Kusha went in to tell their mother Sita that they had brought a beautiful toy to play with. Sita failed to understand what they actually meant by the word 'toy'. Sita was dumb-founded to see Hanuman standing tied outside her hermitage. Seeing Sita alive, Hanuman's joy knew no bounds. He bowed low at her lotus feet and exclaimed, "Mother ! your brave sons had captured the sacrificial horse out of ignorance. That is why this battle was waged against Lord Rama's warriors. These brave sons of yours have defeated Satrughana, Lakshmana and Bharata in the battle. They lie in swoon. That is why Lord Rama has himself arrived to fight against them out of sheer ignorance."

Sita was shocked beyond words on hearing the truth from her most trusted son Hanuman. She was full of anger at the stupidity of her sons. But she was happy to know of their bravery. Her immediate worry was how to stop this battle between the father and his sons.

166. VALMIKI CONSOLING SITA

Hearing the whole tale from his confidential son Hanuman, Sita trembled with great fear and agony. She at once ordered Lava and Kusha to untie and free Hanuman from his bondage. They untied Hanuman but ran out of fear from their mother. Sita rushed in panic to sage Valmiki where she saw her two sons in his company.

Sita narrated the entire story of the battle to the great sage as she had heard it from Hanuman. Falling at his feet she exclaimed, "Revered Rishi ! How is this ignoble battle being fought ? What a shame ! Sons arrayed against father !"

The omniscient sage replied "Dear daughter ! I know everything. Nothing is concealed from my vision. You need not worry at all. I am looking forward to the appropriate moment. Every incident is conducive to your welfare." But Sita exclaimed in a faltering voice, "How after all, grandseer ! My sons have proved to be a slur on the fair name of their dynasty. They have mingled the glory of their uncles into dust. They have caused needless worry to their father. So many soldiers of Ayodhya have been wounded and killed by them. Kindly stop this battle at once."

The Rishi nodded to pacify Sita.

167. VALMIKI CRIES CEASE-FIRE

The next morning Lava and Kusha once again took to the field to resume their unfinished battle. Prior to the commencement of the battle Lava said to Lord Rama, "O great king of Kosala ! If you dare not fight, leave the horse with us and return to your capital. Why do you endanger your life for nothing ?"

Lord Rama smiled and said, "You are still immature children. Such a tall talk is not good for you. Act upon my advice and return home peacefully. Therein lies everybody's welfare."

Lava and Kusha readily retorted, "To flee from the battlefield may suit you. Being warriors, we can't flee the field. Either shall we perish or kill our foes. There is no question of turning our back from the battlefield." Uttering these words the twins shot their arrows at Shri Ramachandra who easily parried them and made them ineffective.

Being enraged at the obstinacy of the twins, Lord Rama set an invincible arrow on his bow. The moment he pulled the arrow to his ear, sage Valmiki appeared on the spot and cried halt to the battle. Lord Rama alighted from his chariot and fell at the feet of the great hermit.

168. RAMA EMBRACES HIS SONS

Valmiki blessed Lord Rama and exclaimed to him, "O illustrious King Ramachandra ! Lava and Kusha are your own sons !" Being surprised as well as elated at this revelation, Lord Rama hugged his dear sons to his bosom.

169. SITA LOST IN THOUGHTS

In the beginning Lord Rama pretended ignorance and asked the sage in surprise, "Are these two boys really my sons ?" Valmiki reaffirmed his assertion and narrated how Lakshmana had left Sita helpless in the dense forest and how he gave shelter to pregnant Sita. Making Brahma, Vishnu and Mahesh a witness, sage Valmiki told Rama that Sita, his beloved queen, gave birth to these twins in his hermitage. He had named them Lava and Kusha and they happened to be as brave and courageous as he himself was.

Then sage Valmiki called Lava and Kusha to his side and bade them thus, "Dear sons ! Prostrate at the lotus feet of your great father Lord Ramachandra, king of Koshala. Ask his forgiveness."

Lord Rama blessed his sons and embraced them to his bosom. The sons too were delighted to be united with their father. Sage Valmiki's penance fructified and his joy was unbounded. He revived Shatrughana, Lakshmana and Bharata from their swoon by sprinkling on them the holy waters of the Ganga. As soon as they got up from their swoon, they fell at the holy feet of sage Valmiki.

Meanwhile Sita too happenend to arrive there. All the three brothers were

overjoyed and fell at Sita's feet. Rama too was delighted to see her but he was still afraid of public slander. So he did not give any expression to his happiness. Sita was shocked at such an attitude displayed by her Lord. Sage Valmiki said to Sita, "Dear daughter ! Blessed you are as you have always meditated upon your Lord. Your conduct has ever been sinless even in your dreams. Nothing is hidden from my divine vision. Your only God has been your husband Lord Rama himself. So I advise you to return to Ayodhya with your sons and husband. Lead a happy life in their company. This is my supreme desire."

Having listened to sage Valmiki's advice, Sita was tempted to go to Ayodhya. She looked at Lord Rama who stood as silent as the hills. Perhaps he was hesitating to take her to Ayodhya. So Sita decided to return to the mother earth who alone could give her shelter.

170. LAKSHMANA PRAYING TO SITA

Sage Valmiki assured Lord Rama that Sita was pure, chaste and sinless. The sage exclaimed, "Great King Rama ! I have undergone severe penances for thousands of years. If Sita has committed any sin even in her dream I may not enjoy the fruit of all my severe penances done so far in my whole life."

Rama replied that he was already convinced of Sita's purity and chastity. But as a king he was afraid of the criticism of his subjects. Then Lord Rama asked Lakshmana to persuade Sita to return to Ayodhya with them. Lakshmana obeyed. He fell at the lotus feet of Sita and said to her, "Mother ! I beg pardon of you. It was I who deserted you in the forest. Now I pray to you to return to Ayodhya with me so that I make amends for the sin I committed."

Sita said, "You did the bidding of Lord Rama who is still indifferent towards me. He never asked me to return to Ayodhya. So how can I ?"

171. SITA PRAYING TO MOTHER EARTH

Inspite of the insistence of Lakshmana, Bharata and Shatrughana, Sita refused to return to Ayodhya as her Lord Rama had not yet asked her even once to come back with him to the capital. Sorrow had broken her heart. Too much of everything is bad. Sita did not wish to mar the righteousness of Lord Rama as a king whose sole duty was to live and act for the happiness of his subjects even at the cost of his personal happiness. Had the rulers of present day world taken a leaf out of Rama's life as a king and acted accordingly, heaven itself would have descended upon the earth.

Greatness of Sita cannot be described in words. She does not wish anything for herself. Her only wish is the glory and greatness for her Lord. So she advanced towards the Sarayu. On her banks she prayed to mother earth in this strain, "If I have never thought of any other man except Lord Rama, goddess Madhavi (Earth) may provide space to me to enter. As I worship Lord Rama in mind, speech and action, O Mother Earth embrace me ! As I have spoken the truth that I do not know any other man except Shri Ramachandra, the earth-goddess may split to take me within her lap." All the gods had assembled on the banks of the Saryu in connection with the oath-taking of Sita. Brahma, the Supreme, was at their head. There were the Adityas, Vasus, Rudras, Visva-devas, Varunas, great sages and the Nagas to witness the truthfulness and purity of Sita. Wearing a brown garment, Sita bowed to all the gods, saints and sages before she took her final oath to prove her purity.

172. SITA EMBRACES MOTHER EARTH

Hearing Sita's oath, the directions trembled. Lightning and thunder flashed across the skies. A sudden earthquake ripped the earth. And out of the womb of the earth came up a divine throne which was borne on the heads by powerful serpents. On that glorious throne the earth-goddess was seated who welcomed her daughter Sita with open arms. Taking Sita into her lap with immense love and affection, the throne went down into the nether-world. A divine shower of flowers covered Sita.

The gods in heaven acclaimed, "Well-done ! Well-done ! O Sita of peerless conduct ! Thou shall be·worshipped till eternity."

Tears streamed from the eyes of the on-lookers. Lava and Kusha wept bitterly and cried loudly. Rama was dumb-founded to see his eternal consort going into the womb of the earth. All kept on gazing till the breach in the earth closed once again.

186

173. RAMA WITH LAVA KUSHA

Rama burst into a rage and exclaimed, "O venerable goddess of Earth ! Please return to me Sita or else grant space to me. I will live with Sita both in the nether-world and in heaven. If you do not give me back my Sita, I will ruin the mountains, forests and the oceans."

Brahma informed Lord Rama that He would again be reunited with Sita in the Heaven. This information pacified him.

When Lord Rama reached Ayodhya with his two sons, he was given a rousing reception. The whole city was decorated and illuminated like a bride as their dear and noble king had got his descendants to the throne. A great procession resembling a marriage passed through the streets of Ayodhya. But Lord Rama within his heart adored Sita. He felt that he could no longer live without her. He was terribly afflicted by Sita's loss. He had no peace of mind. Then came another blow in the death of mother Kaushalya. Sumitra and Kaikeyee also passed away after sometime.

174. RAMA SEEKS FREEDOM FROM WORLDLY DESIRES

Once all of a sudden Lord Rama happened to look himself in the mirror. A sense of renunciation dawned upon him. He had already reigned for eleven thousand years. He wished to return to his Abode—Vishnu Dhaam.

Rama's reign was an ideal one. That is why our leaders aspire to have 'Rama Rajya' even to-day. Throughout the length and breadth of his kingdom people were free from bodily ailments, mental afflictions and natural calamities. They lived in love and co-operation. All were devoted and dedicated to their respective duties and vocations in life. Dharma with its four pillars of *Truth, Purity, Compassion and charity* prevailed everywhere. Not to speak of committing sin, no one even dreamt of it. Poverty, ignorance, illiteracy, diseases and all kinds of sufferings had been banished. In short heaven itself was established on this earth.

Lord Rama who reigned in Ayodhya was the undisputed sovereign of the entire globe girdled by the seven oceans.

175. DHARMRAJA BEFORE VISHNU

Lord Vishnu came to know that Lord Rama on earth wished to return to his abode. He realized that his life span on earth must have been over. So lord Vishnu sent for Narada who fetched Dharm Raja (God of Death) with him. Having bowed to Lord Vishnu, God of Death took his seat.

Then Lord Vishnu said to Dharm Raja, "O God of Death ! Lord Rama has completed his life span on earth. Now you go to the earth and bring him to Heaven with all reverence."

"As you wish my Lord, "Saying so Dharm Raja set out on his mission.

189

176. DHARMRAJA DISGUISES AS BRAHMAN

Dharm Raja dared not disobey Lord Vishnu. But within his heart he was shaken. He said to himself, "How can I tell Lord Rama who is the very embodiment of truth, righteousness and virtue that his life-span on earth is over ? I dare not ask him to accompany me !" But the very next moment he was reminded of the inevitable Law of Nature that he who is born on this earth must depart from it to-day or to-morrow. He sought inspiration from it. So Dharm Raja decided to proceed to Ayodhya all alone. Having reached the borders of Ayodhya, he disguised himself as a Brahman to get entry into proper Ayodhya. As soon as he reached the palace of Lord Rama, Dharm Raja told Lakshmana that he desired to see Lord Rama. The omnipotent and omniscient Rama himself came to the door and bowed to Dharm Raja. He carried him into his palace with great honour.

Lord Rama asked the Brahman how he could serve him. Revealing himself to him Dharm Raja requested him that Lord Vishnu had sent him there with a message which must be delivered to him in utter secrecy.

177. LAKSHMANA GUARDS GATE

Dharm Raja again asserted, "Lord Rama ! None should over hear our conversation. If a third person hears our talks, he shall die at once." Rama understood everything.

He came out to the gate and said to Lakshmana, "Keep standing here at the gate. None should be allowed to come in. He shall indeed be killed who sees or hears the words spoken between the two of us."

Having posted Lakshmana at the gate, Lord Rama requested Dharm Raja to convey Vishu's message to him. Dharm Raja with folded hands exclaimed, "O best among the heroes ! Death has been sent to contact you. If you desire to serve men on the earth for sometime more, you may dwell here as you wish."

Having heard Lord Vishnu's message, Lord Rama spoke thus, "I am filled with great pleasure at your visit. I took human birth to serve the three worlds. Now my mission of service has come to an end. I will go to heaven wherefrom I had come. Infact, I desired that you should call on me. I stayed on the earth to rid the gods of their fear and worry. Nothing remains for me to do now on this earth."

The conversation between Lord Rama and Dharm Raja, the God of Death reveals many things of great significance. First, death is inevitable. He who is born must die sooner or later, today or tomorrow. Second, one need not fear death. Lord Rama is pleased to meet Dharm Raja as this body is no doubt perishable but the soul which is our real nature is imperishable and eternal. So let us not faint when death approaches us. He who can look at death in the face attains immortality. Third, there is a purpose behind this life of ours. That purpose is service to mankind which enables us to attain godhood. He who comes to know that he is not the perishable body but the everlasting soul becomes immortal. The cycle of birth and death stops for him.

178. DURVASA THREATENS LAKSHMANA

While Lord Rama and death-god were talking to each other, the Venerable sage Durvasa appeared at the royal gate. He said to Lakshmana, "Let me see Shri Rama at once." Lakshmana bowing low to Durvasa said, "Pardon me holy sage ! Lord Rama is engaged in very crucial talks with some one at this moment. I cannot enter his chamber to inform him of your arrival."

Durvasa roared, "If you disobey me, I will destroy the whole of Ayodhya. I will curse you as well." But Lakshmana was bent upon doing his duty entrusted to him by Lord Rama. Unable to contain his rage Durvasa uttered the curse, "Lakshmana ! Leave this earth this very moment and go to the Heaven !"

Then he opened the door himself and entered the chamber where Lord Rama was conversing with Death-God.

179. RAMA TALKING TO DURVASA

Rama was amazed to see Durvasa in. But he did not forget to greet him with great reverence. He served him with all kinds of food and drinks as the austere hermit had ended his fast of a thousand years that day. He had come to receive Rama's hospitality before he returned to his heavenly abode. Having consumed nectar-like food served by the Lord himself, the Rishi felt himself blessed indeed.

When Durvasa told Rama that he had cursed Lakshmana to go to heaven with his body, Rama did not relish it. With folded hands he said to Durvasa , "O best among ascetics ! It was not worthy of you. You have committed a grave sin. But mysterious are the ways of destiny ! If you wish like going, you may go. But kindly do not divulge to anybody the secret talks I have had with the Death-God. It will be conducive to your own good." Durvasa felt crestfallen and left the palace in a grave mood. Lakshmana came to Lord Rama and said, "O one of long arms, you should not grieve for me. Desert me O gracious one and keep your promise !"

180. LAKSHMANA GOING TO HEAVEN

Hearing sage Durvasa's curse, Lakshmana was not at all perturbed as he had saved the entire kingdom at the cost of his personal life. What a spirit of patriotism, public welfare and altruism ?

Lord Rama too disowned Lakshmana as a punishment for disobedience as he had failed to prevent Durvasa from getting into his chamber. Lakshmana straight away went to the banks of the Sarayu. Having controlled all his senses, he held his breath. The gods including Indra, the Apsaras and sages showered flowers on him. Taking hold of Lakshmana alive, Indra carried him to Heaven.

Lord Rama, Bharata and Satrughana plunged in the ocean of grief at the departure of Lakshmana. They stood helpless watching Lakshmana going to heaven.

Lord Rama according to his word should have pronounced death sentence on Lakshmana as he could not prevent sage Durvasa from entering his chamber. He had failed to do his duty. But Durvasa had already cursed Lakshmana to go to heaven with his body. So Rama had to disown his dear brother as the wise Hanuman suggested that disowning a dear one was equal to his death. Going to heaven with your body simply means that you die out of your sweet will.

181. RAMA GOING TO SARAYU

Lord Rama crowned Kusha and Lava on the kingdoms of South and North Koshalas.

Rama could not endure the separation of Lakshmana. He spoke thus to the priests, councillors and citizens, "Having crowned Bharata, I will tread on the path that Lakshmana has gone this very day." What a brotherly love !

But Bharata said, "I do not desire kingship or heaven itself in your absence. I will accompany you. Let's send for Shatrughana." What a love for Rama ! But Shatrughana too insisted on going with the Lord.

Then all the subjects said to Lord Rama, "We too will follow you. Take all of us to the forest, fortress or the river or the ocean. But O lord, do not desert us."

Sage Vasishtha also exclaimed, "O child Shri Rama, look at the subjects lying prostrate on the ground. As their king you should act after knowing their intentions. You must not do what is disliked by them."

Inspired by the timely advice of his great Guru, Rama made the subjects rise and said to all of them, "What may I do for you people ?" Then all the subjects said to Lord Rama, "We shall follow you while you go. If you are pleased with the citizens, carry us with you to the heaven where you go."

Seeing the firm devotion of the citizens Lord Rama said to them. "So be it."

182. RAMA MAKES HANUMAN IMMORTAL

Lord Rama advised his friend Vibhishana, "As long as the subjects live you shall remain king of Lanka. Protect your subjects righteously. Worship Vishnu who is all-pervasive and omnipresent."

Then the Lord spoke to his dearest devotee Hanuman, "You have already made up your mind to live on this earth for the sake of devotion to me. As long as my tales are sung on this earth, live here happily." Hanuman's joy knew no bounds as he knew very well that the Lord is endless and so are his tales. So till eternity he (Hanuman) would keep on singing the Lord's name.

Great is the glory of the Ramayana. It gives longevity, riches, power and pelf. He who listens to Rama's noble talks becomes sinless. The Ramayana is as good as the Vedas. A sonless person is blessed with a glorious son on hearing the Ramayana tales. The poor get enriched. Verily the Ramayana contains the essence of the four Vedas, eighteen Puranas, six schools of philosophy and hundred and eight upanishads. He who listens to it or reads it daily with devotion attains the shape of Lord Vishnu Himself. That is why Hanuman preferred to live on earth as Rama's tales are not available in Heaven !

183. RAMA PLUNGES INTO SARAYU

Lord Rama followed by all the citizens of Ayodhya went to the banks of the Sarayu. Rama along with his brothers entered the holy waters of the river. Brahma, the grandfather of the world, accompanied with all the gods came to the place from where Lord Rama was to depart to heaven. He was surrounded by divine chariots in millions as all the subjects, monkeys, bears and animals accompanying Lord Rama were to go to heaven.

Then Brahma said, "O Vishnu come to heaven in any form you like along with your brothers." Then Lord Rama with his brothers entered into Vishnu's form. Then He spoke to Brahma, "You should grant to these hosts of men the highest world as well because they all love me and are my devotees."

Whoever took bath in the waters of the Sarayu ascended the divine chariot. The animals who happened to touch the waters of the Sarayu went to heaven ! Those bears, monkeys and demons who took their bath in the Sarayu entered heaven casting their bodies in the waters.

The citizens who had come to see Lord Rama departing for heaven, they too followed him to heaven by merely seeing him. Such is the power of noble association or Sat-sang. Even those evil spirits who lived there in an invisible way went to heaven as they happened to follow Lord Rama. He who followed the Lord was delivered from bondage.

184. HANUMAN SINGING RAMA

Hanuman became immortal by Lord Rama's grace. It is his pleasure to sing Rama's glory here, there and everywhere on this earth. Wherever the Ramayana is recited or Rama's immortal tales are narrated, Hanuman graces the occasion with his blessed presence. He is the gateway to Godhood. He who worships Hanuman is soon united to Lord Rama.

The Ramayana is a life-giving herb to cure the disease of birth and death. Having listened to this immortal tale of Lord Rama by Lord Shiva himself, mother Parvati declared, "By your blessing, O lord of the universe, I have now attained the ultimate object of my life. Firm devotion to Lord Rama has sprung in my heart and all my troubles and turmoils are over." In this dark age of Kaliyuga no other discipline bears fruit. So Rama alone should be remembered.

Mundane existence is easily crossed over by uttering Rama's name. Rama pervades in every atom of this universe. Let us enthrone Rama, his eternal consort Sita, his brothers Lakshmana, Bharata, Satrughana along with the greatest devotee Hanuman on the throne of our hearts for the sake of bliss everlasting.

OUR OTHER RELIGIOUS BOOKS

Hard Bound Rs. 120   Set of 4 Books Rs. 15 each   Set of 12 Books Rs. 15 each   Set of 12 Books Rs. 15 each

Gita, Shri Krishna Leela, Ramayana and Mahabharata are our other publications in the series of religious books. Each book is unique by virtue of four-colour illustrations and easy-to-understand subject-matter. Each book has been put in a nutshell for the sake of the readers keeping in view the fact that it does not miss any relevant information.

Rs. 40   Rs. 40   Rs. 40   Rs. 40

These are four books based on Hindu deities. Each books studies the birth and exploits of a particular deity. Colourful illustrations and easy-to-understand text matter add lustre to these religious books.